Ghosts on the Cumberland: Frights and Tales from the Dark Waters

By

John Leslie Oliver

Deep Read Press

www.deepreadpress.com

615-670-1725

LAFAYETTE, TENNESSEE
deepreadpress@gmail.com

First Deep Read Press Edition.

Published in the United States of America

Edited by: Shena Newberry Wilder

Cover Design by: Kim Gammon

ISBN (Paperback): 978-1-954989-33-7

ISBN (Hardback): 978-1-954989-34-4

Published by:
DEEP READ PRESS

Lafayette, Tennessee
www.deepreadpress.com
deepreadpress@gmail.com

This book is for those who want to believe in ghosts, who want to think that dark nights hold a spirit world of restless souls, but hesitate to fully believe until they meet a ghost in person, face to face. These stories may push you, the reader, to become a 'true believer' or they may just entertain you...in either case, I dedicate this collection of stories to you. Enjoy!

Table of Contents

What Makes a Ghost A Ghost?

In collecting the stories for a book such as this, one has to first determine, just what is a 'ghost'?

While the image of a spectral figure in white, hovering over a tombstone may come to mind, as you will see in exploring the subject, a ghost may be the sound of footsteps on the stairs when there is no one in the house but you; or a light that moves about in the forest where a local murder was committed; or the covers snatched off your bed in the middle of the night and it wasn't the cat!

Noises, voices in the dark, strange lights, items moved about the house or just an eerie sensation down your spine as you walk past a cemetery...we can be convinced that something strange is going on. And, we may blame it on the neighborhood ghost.

Having witnessed a few unexplained sounds and lights myself, I can't testify in court, under oath, that ghosts don't exist...can you?

We acknowledge that not every departed soul in the graveyard returns to scare the daylights out of us, but the few ghosts we do whisper about on a dark and gloomy night tend to have one thing in common...the dead person was the victim of a gruesome, unsolved, peculiar or undeserving death.

So, it is, that murderers or their victims rise up on moonless nights to tap us on the shoulder and tell us their tragic circumstances; or, the lonely maiden who died an old woman waiting for her lover to return home from battle sits forlornly by the window; or the worker crushed beneath the wheels of a train whose body parts were never found...at least not all of them...walks the rails at night.

They are never content to rise to their heavenly home above, or sink to the fiery depths below, until they have wailed and moaned here on earth unless one night they tire of their lonely between world's existence and finally 'give up the ghost'!

Ghosts may suddenly appear or only show themselves to certain people. They may disappear as mysteriously as they first arrived on the scene. They may move the furniture, turn on the radio, sing to music only they can hear, pace up and down the hallway or simply sit on their tombstones waiting for the right person to come along and talk to them.

As far as I can tell, ghosts seldom harm anyone...although being scared half to death may be as close to the 'hereafter' as you may wish to be. Yet, there is the occasional ghost who waits in the dark for the very person who caused their demise with the sole intention of returning the favor.

Our hope, is that when walking one dark night, past the tree where a man was hung, that we don't resemble the person who tied the rope around their neck, lest they think they have found their man!

It makes me jittery to think about it.

Maybe these stories will entertain you, perhaps make you chuckle or even laugh...not out loud, we hope...or maybe they will make you look about the room as you read because you just heard a creaking floor board or a wisp of cold air crossed your cheek, or maybe they will make you pull the quilts up over your head as you lie down to sleep.

Sweet dreams, my dear!

The Cumberland River

You can go almost anywhere in the American South and find someone who can tell you a good ole' ghost story!

We all enjoy a little scare, whether it's to put us in the mood for the Halloween season, or we only wish to frighten our little brother just before his bedtime.

We limit ourselves in this book to ghost stories found in the lands adjacent to the Cumberland River, from its headwaters above Burnside, Kentucky, as it snakes its way through Tennessee, till it flows into the Ohio River at Smithland, once again in Kentucky.

That is 688 miles of slow moving water, lapping at the banks of farmland, forest, lake (it is impounded to make Lakes Barkley, Old Hickory and Cumberland), cities, suburbs, industrial parks and recreation areas.

This source for tales of ghostly encounters is enough for our volume without having to go far from shore.

We have combed old newspapers, diaries, letters and books and interviewed people from here to there.

Which leads us to make an important distinction in recounting such tales...there are the stories we tell on the back porch to our friends and those we listen to spoken with authority by a person whose voice commands our attention when they say, “this happened to me one dark night...”

The former stories, are those told in the dark, on a hot summer night when the only light is that from the moon or a passing lightening bug. They are “Let me tell you a good old ghost story...” stories!

These are usually vague as to where they happened, exactly when, or even who the original victim of the scare was.

The teller may declare, “I swear this is the truth...”, but when interrogated admit, “I was told this in camp...” or some such place.

We lump those stories into the realm of “it makes a good story, but...”

Such stories are not included in this collection, although it’s hard to beat the old ‘who’s got my liver?’ ghost story as the teller jumps up from their seat and hollers, “You have it!” to the squeals of fear and delight from those gathered around.

Instead, in these pages we only include stories handed down and written down from one generation to another, tales about real people in specific places with unexplainable causes.

We document those, but will keep some details to ourselves so as to prevent a crew of cameramen and erstwhile reporters from descending on the front yards of those who have confided in us.

Certain locations and names we do give, because their stories, such as that of the Bell Witch, are already known and they are prepared for any additional publicity.

But, before you begin reading this collection, let me warn you...be careful not to sit in a dark room by yourself with only the light of a solitary lamp. The subject matter we present can put goosebumps on even the most skeptical of readers.

I give you this example:

As a young fellow, I was a Scoutmaster and had the fortune to have a large cabin down by Old Hickory Lake offered to us for one night so I could take the boys fishing and have the comforts that a roof over our heads and indoor plumbing provide.

It was just myself and about a dozen young charges, mostly ten to twelve years old.

Using the large living room of the cabin as our place to bed down, the boys all unrolled their sleeping bags and arranged them around the room, noticeably away from me, to be beside their best friends, etc.

Undaunted by the lack of companionship, I was joyful in that I had commandeered the plush couch against one wall and, rolling out my own sleeping bag, was ready for a good night's sleep.

After plenty of talking, joking around and snacks I told the boys it was time to turn off the lights and go to sleep.

The usual protests were made and someone yelled out, "Let's all tell ghost stories!"

I agreed and stated quite firmly, "OK guys, two or three and that's it."

I opened the floor to volunteers and the stories began.

Being older and, I hope, wiser, I was sorely disappointed by what they provided. Nothing new there, just the classic ghostly hitch-hiker type stuff.

Disappointed, I decided to tell one myself, but I wasn't going to repeat some tale of strange lights in a graveyard. I decided to go in for the kill!

I said, out loud, "My turn!"

Then, "But first, let's turn out the lights."

Using my best, 'Now Boys, this actually happened' voice I proceeded to tell the gullible listeners about a group of Boy Scouts...how appropriate...who were out camping one night next to this very lake...coincidence, you say...and their gristly murders at the hands of an escapee from an insane asylum.

This was before Hollywood gave us "Friday the 13th" or "Nightmare on Elm Street," but my tale would have made them look like nursery rhymes.

Of course, I made it up as I went along.

I only noticed one thing as I wound my story to its end, the room had gotten extremely quiet.

"The killer has never been caught, " I finished up and added that the killer was believed to still be roaming the woods close by, "which is why", I mentioned casually, "we were given this nice cabin for the night, because the owners haven't been back since the night they heard something outside and saw a pair of eyes peering in the big picture window...the one overlooking the lake...the one over there across the room." The boys were silent.

Then I heard a lone voice, barely audible, "Mr. Oliver, could you switch on the lights? I gotta pee and I'm not walking across this room in the dark!"

I reached for the light switch and flicked the lights on.

To my amazement, I saw that every last one of the scouts was now within five feet of me and the couch, their sleeping bags scrunched up about them and their backs to me, with their faces glued to that big picture window across the room, the one overlooking the lake.

I had, unwittingly, scared the daylights out of them!

Now, hear my words of caution, despite my laughs at their relocations and despite my admission that, "I made the whole thing up," the boys were convinced that there was something out there in the dark.

The power of suggestion!

By the way, we slept that night with the lights on!

Loch Lomond

The Bloody Hands of the Duke of Cumberland!

"The Duke of Cumberland" was one of the titles given to Prince William, the third son of King George II of England in the 1700's.

He is also known by the not so polite, "the butcher Cumberland".

Prince William is important to our collection of ghost stories because he is the believed namesake for the river in the title of this book.

Explorer Thomas Walker, who in 1750 was the first white man to explore the wooded hills of what are today, Kentucky and Tennessee, gave the Duke's name to the river he spied on his travels.

The duke is the source of more than a name!

In the mid 1700's, there was a dispute between Prince William's father, the King, and 'Bonnie Prince Charlie', who claimed that the throne of England belonged to him.

Bonnie Prince Charlie was Scottish.

His followers were called 'Jacobites.'

The English called Charlie, 'the Pretender', because he went around pretending he was the rightful king.

In 1746, Bonnie Prince Charlie and his small army of Jacobites started a revolution.

The Pretender and his Scottish Highlanders... so called because they came from the highlands of Scotland...were doomed from the start.

Badly outnumbered, Charlie met the English army at a place called Culloden.

The English army, in uniform, with cannon and rifles with bayonets, charged the Highlanders, who stood out in their Scottish plaid kilts.

In the background, the Highlanders and Bonnie Prince Charlie, could hear the sad sounds of the bagpipes, played by their fellow Scots.

And, you may have guessed by now, the man who led the better equipped English army against the Pretender and his kilt wearing Scots...was Prince William, the Duke of Cumberland.

The Battle of Culloden lasted less than an hour; Bonnie Prince Charlie was forced to flee for his life; and those Jacobites who weren't killed or wounded ran for their lives back to the highlands of Scotland.

And, it was then that the bloody hands of the Duke earned him his moniker, 'the butcher Cumberland'.

Seeing the battlefield strewn with the bodies of the dead Scots and those too wounded to flee, he ordered his soldiers to finish the job they had started and to use their swords to slay any man of the enemy left alive on the ground.

He was a butcher indeed.

He ordered his army to pursue those who had fled and put them to the sword too.

Those who aided or helped the fleeing Jacobites were killed, imprisoned or shipped off to the colonies.

The wearing of plaid kilts was outlawed and even bagpipes were seized and destroyed.

Bonnie Prince Charlie, the Pretender, managed to escape Scotland and find refuge in Europe, but he never raised an army again.

Eventually, tensions between Scotland and England eased and by the 1820's, the bagpipe and plaids were once again Scottish traditions and continue to be so to this day.

Now, what does this have to do with ghosts?

People who live near the old battlefield of Culloden will tell you they hear the sounds of battle still...on dark nights when the moon is just a sliver or slides behind a cloud.

The cries of dying men, they say, still carry across the barren ground.

A man wearing a Scottish plaid kilt can be seen walking around the earthen mounds where the dead were piled and dirt tossed on top, like a dark blanket over their bloody corpses.

It is said that to this day, birds avoid those same earthen burial mounds and refuse to sing when passing by.

Which brings us to our last bit of lore on the bloody duke.

Perhaps the best known song of old Scotland is "The Bonnie, Bonnie Banks of Loch Lomond."

A 'loch' is a lake and Loch Lomond is the largest lake in Scotland and well known for its beauty.

In the song, a lover tells us that they will meet us again on the banks of Loch Lomond, but while we 'take the high road', they will 'take the low road'.

The song is a Jacobite version of an older melody and the 'low road' is a metaphor for 'death', that is, the lover will meet us again one day, but they will be taking the 'low road' for they have died fighting for Bonnie Prince Charlie...killed by 'the butcher Cumberland'!

Spearfinger

The land drained by the Cumberland River was occupied by Native Americans for many thousands of years.

The history of the First Peoples is that of a people who occupied a new world and adapted to its wildlife, climate and terrain. From the snow and ice of the artic to the jungles of the Amazon, the First Peoples made their homes and raised their families.

There are secessions of different groups, or tribes, that occupied what are now Tennessee and Kentucky, but the last groups are the ones we are most familiar with. They were the tribes that resisted the waves of Europeans who sought to lay a claim to their ancestral lands.

The valleys of the Cumberland sheltered the Cherokee, the Shawnee and the Chickasaw.

Each tribe had differences in the way they dressed, their language and their traditions...and each one had their own legends, and even their own ghostly stories.

'Spearfinger' is one of those!

As with all tribes, evenings would likely find little Cherokee children playing games until either the dark or the chill of the evening led them to seek the safety and warmth of a fire.

There, an older family member might tell stories to entertain the children... and, one of the stories they would tell was the legend of 'Spearfinger'.

The Cherokee believed in many mystical creatures. Some of these were similar to monsters and were deadly to the Cherokee people. Sometimes these creatures were associated with particular mountains, river bluffs or unusual natural features of the land, such as a waterfall or cave.

The most feared of all the Cherokee monsters was 'Utluhtu' or 'Spearfinger'.

Spearfinger was a 'shape changer' and could turn herself into any living thing. But, when she was being herself, she was a little old woman with a particularly long bony finger on one hand...hence, the name 'Spearfinger'.

This finger was evil, for she would use it to stab someone and pull their liver out, which she would then eat. People who were touched by this wicked finger didn't always realize what had happened, but would begin to waste away and eventually die, for no one can live without their liver!

Because Spearfinger would appear before people in her natural shape, as an old woman, they would not realize how dangerous she was until it was too late.

Something had to be done about her.

A group of brave men of the Cherokee people got together and laid a trap for Spearfinger.

They built a fire close by a deep pit and covered the pit with brush to conceal it. Spearfinger saw the fire and suspected it was the fire of some hunters and she plotted to enter their camp and then touch one of them to get his liver for her supper.

Not seeing the pit because it was so cleverly hidden, she fell into it and the hidden men sprang into action. They began to shoot arrows into Spearfinger, trying to kill her to keep her from harming anyone else.

But, her skin was hard and the arrows bounced off of her and her tough old hide.

A tiny bird, a titmouse, was watching the men and began to sing loudly. The bird repeated one note over and over and to the men it sounded like the Cherokee word for 'heart' and thinking the bird was giving them a clue, they aimed for Spearfinger's heart...but, to no avail.

In anger the men repaid the titmouse for his lie by cutting off his tongue, and to this day, all titmouse have short tongues!

Seeing the predicament, the men were having, another bird, a chickadee, decided to help and it flew into the pit where it landed on the evil Spearfinger's hand.

The braves thought the chickadee's behavior odd, but then realized this bird might be trying to tell them something. They began to aim their arrows at the wicked hand and its deadly finger.

One arrow hit the very spot where the evil finger joined the scrawny withered old hand and when it did, old Spearfinger died instantly.

"To this day," the old Cherokee storyteller would whisper to the children gathered around, "the chickadee is treasured by the Cherokee people as a truth teller and a bearer of good news."

A Haunted House

Hollywood movies and television shows love a good haunted house. They are usually abandoned Victorian mansions with many rooms, layers of dust and spider webs and, oh yes...ghosts.

Real haunted houses are rarely like that.

The ghosts in this story from Burkesville, Kentucky, a town on the headwaters of the Cumberland River, inhabited a simple house and the ghosts had a reason for showing up when people dropped by.

In the old days, people might live their whole life in the same house...born, raised and died there!

If you were to look at an ancient home for sale today, don't ask the real estate agent if anyone had ever died in the home because the answer might shock you.

Before hospitals and nursing homes, the sick and elderly were expected to die at home.

Usually, these people would pass away with their family close by, perhaps sitting by the bed, holding the hand of the person as they took their last breath.

But, sometimes death came unannounced and when it did, the victim might have had a secret, a secret that they took to the grave with them!

In this story a man has either inherited or purchased a little old house but he couldn't get anyone to live there. It seems people would claim that the little cottage was haunted!

After a while, in desperation, the landlord simply offered the house and its small lot to anyone who could stay one whole night there. Well, the offer of a free home might be pretty enticing...unless, of course, it is rumored to be haunted.

According to the story, as it has been passed down, there were a few people who tried, but no one was able to spend a full night there.

That is, until a new resident came to Burkesville...a preacher man.

Not put off by the age of the old house or its dilapidated conditions, the preacher met with its owner and they shook hands on the deal. The house would be his if he could stay the night.

So, armed with nothing more than his Bible, the preacher entered the house and built a good fire in the fireplace and after lighting a dust covered ancient oil lamp, sat down in a rickety old chair and began to read his holy book.

Maybe it was at midnight, the witching hour, or maybe it was earlier, but at some time in the night the door to the upstairs swung open.

A little scary perhaps!

Maybe it's the wind, the preacher must have reasoned and he continued to read.

Then a ghostly looking dog came down the stairs and sat down by the fireplace!

But, our God fearing man wasn't alarmed and keeping one eye on the strange dog, continued to read his Bible, as if this was nothing to be alarmed by.

And then a ghostly man came down the stairs and stood in the middle of the room, staring at our man in the chair.

Now, for most of us, that would have been the straw that broke the camel's back!

Many of us would have never gone into a haunted house, alone, at night!

Many more of us would have fled when the door to the stairs flew open. You would have seen how fast we could run!

Many of those still there would have panicked when a ghost dog came down those stairs and sat beside the fire...but, if there was anyone still sitting in that chair when a strange ghostly man got to the bottom of those stairs, they wouldn't have still been there when he walked to the center of the room and stood there staring!

The preacher, however, was undaunted!

Maybe he knew the 'good book' was his protection, or maybe he sensed something else, because he stared back at the man and calmly said, "What in the name of the Lord, do you want?"

The man of the cloth knew something about people, and what makes them do strange things. This here ghost was there for a purpose, the preacher reckoned, so he simply asked the ghost...and, the ghost answered!

"Come with me!" the ghost spoke and he motioned the preacher to follow him as he turned and walked to another door, the door to the cellar.

Those of us who may have made it this far would likely not have gone a step further...follow a dead man down the steps to a dark old cellar!

You've got to be kidding!

Yet, the preacher man did as the ghost requested.

Once there, the strange man pointed to a place on the earthen floor of the cellar and said, "Dig here!"

Well, the preacher did and he found an earthenware pot.

He pulled it out of the dirt and removed its lid.

It was full of money!

We might mention here that in the old days, few towns had banks and people often kept what money they had, hidden about their homes.

We know of a man who drilled holes in the logs of his smokehouse and filled them with silver dollars and then plugged the holes with mud. He did that to keep Bushwackers from finding his money during the Civil War!

Many a story has been told about families who buried their valuables in the backyard during those troubling times for the same reason... both Yankee and Confederate scavengers would raid a home looking for money or jewels or silver.

The ghost in the little old house of our story wanted to see his long buried wealth dug up and put to good use.

Well, we would expect that there was no better person to do that than a man of God...and, in that case, we would be right!

As the story comes to us, that is just what happened.

The new preacher in Burkesville got the house and the money and used the money to start a church right there in town.

As for the ghosts, well, as we are led to believe, their days of haunting were over and the man and his ghostly dog were finally content to stay in their graves.

The Girl at The Window

Several things contribute to this ghost story from Russell County, Kentucky...windows, lightening and a girl's anger!

If you visit a really old home and chance to look out the window, you might think that the view is a little twisted or warped. That would be because the old glass was hand blown and cut to size. Hand blown glass will have small ripples or waves.

Modern technology has improved glass to the nice flat surface we see today.

Antique furniture can be dated by the wavy glass in its cabinet doors. Old homes may have the same rippled glass in their windows.

The old house and old windows of this story have more than a slight distortion due to hand blown glass...they also have the image of a dead person!

In this legend, passed around for generations, a girl on the edge of becoming a young lady, was excited to be going to a party one Saturday night. It may have been a dance or just a social get-to-gather, but as the story is generally told, she expected to meet a boy there. That adds an element of interest to our story!

She is anxious, as all young lovers are, to see her 'beau'.

But, things got complicated the afternoon of the party when the skies blackened and the wind picked up. Soon, rain began to pour down and thunder and lightning could be heard in the distance.

Her parents, cautious as to the dangers of traveling by horse and buggy during a storm, told her that if it didn't let up soon, she couldn't go to the party.

Thunder and lightning, we all know, are unpredictable.

Upset, the girl retreated upstairs to her bedroom in the attic.

The storm continued to rumble, the thunder shaking the house and the lightning flashing its garish yellow light.

Angry, she stood in front of her bedroom window, looking out.

There are several versions of this story, but a common theme is that the girl, mad at the thought of not seeing her sweetheart, cursed the storm. No sooner had the words left her mouth than a bolt of lightning hit the earth just outside the house and traveled through the window where the girl stood, striking her.

She screamed and fell to the floor!

Her parents rushed upstairs to investigate only to find their daughter dead.

The twist to our story is that when the lightning passed through the window, the girl's image was somehow burned onto one of the glass panes.

It wasn't recognized at first.

Several weeks later, on a stormy day just like the day the young girl was killed, as the rain trickled down the glass, the family saw her image in the window!

The story of her death and the lightning's eerie effect quickly passed through the community and is repeated to this day.

Unlike most of the ghosts we have encountered, this dead person doesn't walk through a room or shriek in the night. She doesn't make a sound.

Rather, she lies in her grave close by, as the rain forever paints her image on the window as if to taunt her for losing her temper at the whims of nature.

The Ghost of a Little Black Dog

There are plenty of spooky tales across the state of Kentucky, tales of ghosts that dart between the tombstones of ancient cemeteries or mysterious lights that hover over the graves of murdered men and women.

The Cumberland River begins in the hills and hollers of that fine state, passing through Pulaski, Wayne, Russell, Cumberland, Clinton, and Monroe Counties.

Tompkinsville is Monroe county's largest town, but within its borders it has a wealth of small communities with quaint names such as Gumtree, Coon's Foot, Bugtussle, Stringtown, Mud Lick, and Meshack.

The ghostly black dog of our story may have come from one of these uniquely named little communities, because it is the tale of a Monroe County ghost.

Like so many ghost stories, this one starts with a murder.

What makes a man take another man's life?

Well, perhaps it was a long standing grudge or maybe a wrong word spoken when the other fellow was in a bad mood. Often, there was a little moonshine involved because, as we all know, when moonshine wets the lips, it also loosens the tongue and men say things drunk that they wouldn't say sober.

We know the killer was a man named Crawford.

And, we know that the victim had a dog...a little black dog.

Maybe the dog wouldn't leave his dead master's body and maybe that black dog growled and barred its teeth whenever Crawford tried to get close to it so he could dispose of it...we don't know.

But, we do know this, Crawford killed the little black dog too.

Crawford threw the man's body and the body of the little black dog into a pond close by.

In the hills of Kentucky there are a lot of superstitions about dead people.

They say that grass won't grow where a dead body has lain on the ground.

Don't step over a grave!

That's bad luck for sure!

Crawford must have thought he was pretty clever to toss those two bodies in the pond. Must have weighted them down with rocks because we all know that on the third day, a body in water will rise to the surface.

Some people say a roll of thunder will pull a drowned man's body up from the dark depths.

In the old days, people would fire a cannon to get a drown body to rise up.

One thing for sure, though, that dead man's ghost didn't stay put.

We know that because a few days after the gruesome double murder, Crawford stepped out on his porch and looked in the direction of the pond and he saw them...the dead man and his little black dog, standing there, staring right back at him!

It seems that every time Crawford looked in that direction, to where the muddy pond lay, he would see that dead man and his dog.

Nobody else, it seems, noticed anything.

They may have wondered what happened to one of their neighbors and his little black dog. “They went everywhere together,” they likely said. “Ain’t seen ‘em in several days, though.”

We all know that a person’s mind can play tricks on them, especially when they have a heap of guilt a weighing on it, just like the rocks a weighing down the body of that poor murdered man and his little black dog.

Crawford decided to do something about his little predicament. He left town!

Went to Missouri, they say.

That should have solved the problem.

But, it didn’t!

Two days after he got to Missouri, Crawford looked out a window and saw the ghostly forms of the dead man and his little black dog.

The ghosts had followed him to Missouri!

The way the story has been passed down, Crawford stayed there for quite a while and the ghosts stayed right there with him.

It may be that Crawford only saw them on dark nights or only when his conscience got the best of him, or maybe when he had done a little drinking, but after a while he decided to return to Monroe County, Kentucky.

Once he was back, he was with a friend and the two of them happened to be near a pond, the same pond where Crawford had tossed the bodies.

The friend looked up and saw a strange dog...a little black dog.

All of a sudden, it was just there.

Oh yes, one more thing.

The little black dog had a bone its mouth, a big bone.

The dog stared at the two men.

Ole Crawford started to look awful pale. He recognized that dog...it was the little black dog that he had killed and thrown into the pond along with its owner. It was the same little black dog that had followed him to Missouri and now it was right there in front of him.

The other man said, "I don't understand why that dog is carrying that bone around! Do you know what he's carrying it for?"

Crawford snapped back, "No, I don't!"

Then the visitor looked at that dog and that big bone and said, "He come out of that pond with that bone. Something has been put in that pond, or somebody has killed somebody; and that's somebody's bone. Ain't no hog bone!"

Right then and there, Crawford fell to his knees and began to weep. He was so full of guilt and worry from that dog's ghost that he was overcome.

"What's the matter with you?" the friend said.

Crawford couldn't hold in his guilt any longer. He confessed right then and there to the murder of the man and his little black dog!

So, that's the end of our little ghost story.

Crawford went to jail for the murder and as for the ghosts of the man and his little black dog, it is supposed that they found their peace and have finally disappeared.

But, if I lived in Monroe County, Kentucky, I wouldn't hang around any old farm ponds on a dark lonely night...just in case!

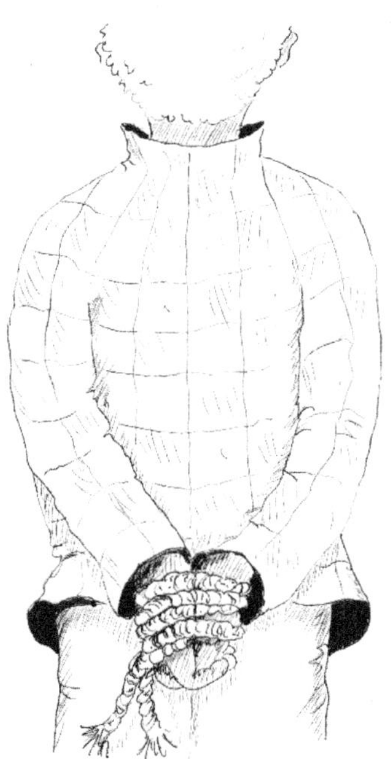

My Hands Are Tied

The Cumberland River begins in the hills of Kentucky and passes through the Cumberland Plateau into Tennessee, where the hillsides and small valleys...called 'hollers' as a regional dialect for 'hollow'...lend themselves to isolation.

Isolation may have been what lead Virginia Hill to purchase two thousand acres of land in what is now Clay County, Tennessee.

The year was 1816.

Although Virginia Hill was from a wealthy North Carolina family, she likely didn't have to pay much for those two thousand acres. Who would want to live so far away from civilization and live on those rock strewn hills, hills so steep that folks say that to keep from falling over, the cows have legs longer on one side than the other!

Virginia Hill brought her slaves with her, for she had a purpose for moving there. Upon her arrival, she freed her slaves. She turned the land over to them, to live on and to hopefully, thrive. Maybe there, they would be safe from the slave owning people in the counties and states around them.

The isolation of those two thousand acres was good for her purpose. For, who would want to take that land away from them? Who would be jealous of those high rocky hills and deep hollers?

Perhaps there was another reason for Virginia seeking that remote area. Oral legend says that some of the mulatto children in the group were actually members of Virginia's own family!

The Obey Rivers meets the Cumberland River in Celina, just a few miles from the land Virginia Hill purchased. Today, those two thousand acres are known as 'Free Hill, Tennessee.'

The little community of freed slaves did manage to scratch out a living and in the years after the Civil War, it grew to three hundred residents and even had its own school in the years of segregation.

As former slaves and the children of slaves, the people of Free Hill would have known the ghost stories and traditions of their native Africa and would have learned stories from their white owners and overseers.

They would have heard and repeated our next story, which goes like this...

Two young slaves on a big plantation pledged their love for each other.

They worked on the same large farm and would have seen each other in the fields, at church and at weekend get togethers when someone would pull out a banjo and they could sing and dance.

Hoping to have the master of the estate give them permission to wed when they got old enough, they swore to each other their undying love.

Yet, despite their vows to be true to each other, the boy cheated on his sweetheart while on a visit to a neighboring farm.

When she found out, she was brokenhearted.

But, she was also mad…very mad!

She told her boyfriend…we'll call him Thaddeus…she told him, "Thaddeus, you have gone and broke my poor little heart! You need to be punished if you ever expect to kiss my lips again!"

Poor Thaddeus, was he to lose his love for his little sweetheart? We'll call her Eliza Mae.

"Oh, Eliza Mae!" he lamented. "Please forgive me! I'll take whatever punishment you want to inflict on my ole' worthless hide!"

Thaddeus didn't realize the implications of what he had just said, he was so anxious to win back her love.

"Whatever?" Eliza Mae asked.

"Whatever!" he answered.

She told Thaddeus to meet her later that day, about dusk, down by the river, on a bluff overlooking a spot where the river was swift and cold.

He did as he was told, happy to let her hit him a few times with her fists or maybe a big stick. If that got him back in her good graces, it was worth it. Besides, how hard could that pretty little gal hit him?

Once there Thaddeus didn't see the bedevilment in her eyes. He just listened as she told him to turn his back to her and he stood quietly as she took a short piece of rope and tied his hands together behind him.

Then, with her anger deep and malevolent, she led him to the edge of the bluff...to the very edge.

"Close your cheatin' eyes, Thaddeus! I don't want you to see what I'm about to do!" she said.

Thaddeus obeyed.

Eliza Mae backed up a few feet from her lover and put both her hands out in front of her.

You see, it was her intention to push Thaddeus off that cliff and into the deep cold water below, knowing that with his hands tied, he wouldn't be able to swim or grab onto the steep sides of the bluff.

He would drown for sure!

But, Eliza Mae wasn't too concerned about that, as there was another boy on the plantation that had recently caught her eye!

Standing there, poor Thaddeus thought about his situation. What did his Eliza Mae have in mind?

Was she just trying to scare him?

Confused, he opened one eye and glanced back behind him to see what Eliza Mae was doing.

Then, just as she took a run towards him, he panicked and stepped aside. Poor Eliza May! Her momentum was too strong for her to stop and she plunged off the bluff to the water below!

Dumbstruck by what had happened, ole Thaddeus looked down below as Eliza Mae went under the water and then came back to the top, sputtering water from her mouth and crying out, "Oh, Thaddeus, save me! I can't swim. Oh, Thaddeus, do something!"

Now, that ole Thaddeus wasn't as foolish as we might be thinking. Seeing what had just transpired, he realized she had meant to push him off that bluff and to let him drown.

Shaking his head, he mournfully hollered back, "Oh Lord, my poor little Eliza Mae. I can't do nothing to help you...my hands are tied!" Sure enough. He spoke the truth.

His hands were tied. Eliza Mae had tied them herself.

And, to her dismay, she drowned.

The former slaves of Free Hill would have laughed at this story.

Well, some ghost stories do make us laugh, and if her ghost lingers on a bluff by the river, we might be tempted to laugh too. But, we wouldn't let her ghost see us chuckle, lest she was still angry!

Hugh Rogan's Stone Cottage

An Irishman Comes to Tennessee, Hugh Rogan

This story starts with a man from Ireland...a man named Hugh Rogan.

Ireland's history is a troubled one, indeed, and due to wars and politics, most land in the 1700's was in the hands of wealthy Englishmen who rented it out to the Irish people...sometimes at soul crushing rents.

Hugh Rogan left his wife and infant son in Ireland to travel to the colonies in what are now the United States, where he hoped to one day own land of his own and not pay the high rents so many of his countrymen faced.

He immediately got caught up in the American Revolution and when the frontier opened up for settlement, Hugh Rogan was there. He soon found himself in Middle Tennessee, in what is now Sumner County.

More than once did he escape the tomahawk of the Native Americans, but he eventually laid claim to 1,000 acres, a piece of land close by the banks of the Cumberland River.

When he was secure in its ownership, he set out for Donegal, back in his homeland of Ireland, to fetch his wife and son.

The story goes that in Virginia, on his way to an Eastern port, he ran into an old acquaintance from Donegal who told Hugh that his wife, not having heard from him for several years, had presumed he was dead and had remarried.

A saddened man, Hugh returned to Middle Tennessee and his farm.

But, our story has a twist.

For whatever reason, the old acquaintance had given Hugh Rogan the wrong story. His wife and son were still awaiting his return.

In some manner Hugh found out the truth and after a separation of 21 years, he traveled back to Ireland and brought his wife and now grown son back with him.

Now, with his family intact, Hugh Rogan did a most peculiar thing...he built a house.

That of course, is not peculiar in and of itself, except that Hugh Rogan built an Irish house!

No hand-hewn log home like his neighbors, but a rock house like the one he had grown up in...a stone house with a large central chimney and a big room to each side.

The stone was quarried from the limestone bluffs found all through Middle Tennessee and cut to size with rock hammers and iron tools, each stone smooth faced and stacked layer upon layer.

And, in their new home, he and his wife Ann welcomed a second son, born over twenty years after his older brother!

Our story has another twist.

The durability of a stone house to withstand the elements was proven when, almost two centuries later, it was still standing, though no longer occupied.

I recall seeing the old home myself, when it was pointed out to me on a drive through the Sumner County countryside, years ago.

Our second twist is that, the stone cottage, being a piece of local and state history for its uniqueness, was disassembled, moved and rebuilt a few miles down the road at Bledsoe's Fort Historic Park, in Sumner County. It lies beside State Highway 25 in the Castalian Springs community, outside Gallatin.

Visitors to the park can see it today, looking just as it did around 1800, and furnished as Ann Rogan would have.

Which brings us to our ghost story, for you see, the Irish know all about spirits, fairies and 'things that go bump in the night.'

For example, Hugh and Ann Rogan would have been told the legend of the 'banshee' from the time they were wee children, for all Irish knew that if a person hears the sorrowful screams of the banshee it means that their death is imminent.

Described as being an old woman with tattered dress and long wild looking hair, the banshee's scream is only heard by those doomed to die...a warning you might say, to put their affairs in order for their remaining time on earth is short.

Let's step back in time and go inside Hugh and Ann Rogan's stone cottage. If we do we will observe their behavior when a member of the family died.

They would immediately draw the curtains of the house.

Ann would have then covered all the mirrors in the house lest the departing soul see its reflection and gets caught.

Hugh Rogan would have stepped to the fireplace mantle and stopped the pendulum on the clock that set there. That was done to fool the devil and allow the soul of the dead person to travel to heaven before the devil knew they were dead!

A tricky lot the Irish!

With the curtains closed, the rooms are now dark and candles would be lit and placed in the room with the dead body so it wouldn't be frightened by the dark...and it would be the responsibility of the family to always have someone sitting with the body, so it won't be lonely.

The deceased would be washed and dressed in their best clothes.

A simple wood coffin would be brought into the house and set upon chairs turned inward.

Black ribbons would be hung on the outside doors so neighbors would know that someone had died, and now, the 'wake' would begin.

A 'wake' was a traditional mourning and celebration of the life of the deceased. A bit of Irish whisky might be poured into cups for all who visited and wished to partake of a drink in memory of the deceased lying there in the open coffin.

With the evening, a fiddler might be present to play a few tunes while there would be tears and even some laughter as visitors and family would recall better times with the departed soul.

Burial would take place the next day, as this was before funeral homes and preserving the body with embalming.

When the pall bearers arrived, they would lift the casket and then kick over the chairs that had held it, so that any spirits hanging around would not have a place to sit and would have to leave the house with the funeral procession.

Then, very importantly, the coffin is carried out the door feet first, so that the dead one has to face outwards and is not able to look back at the house and beckon anyone there to follow them to the grave.

Yet, the old beliefs are not over.

When buried in the churchyard, as many cemeteries were beside a church, it was the Irish belief that the most recently buried in the cemetery would have to toil for all the dead already there, until another person would pass away and inherit the task from them.

And, what would the dead in a cemetery be wanting?

Since the Irish were mostly Catholic and a Catholic believes in 'purgatory', a place where people might be stuck between heaven and hell, they might have to haul water to the dead, for those in purgatory thirst while waiting to enter their eternal home.

Once the funeral was over, the family would return home and the curtains opened once more, the black ribbons removed from the doors and the chairs set up right.

One last thing!

Ann Rogan would have taken the bits of candle left from the wake and placed them in a special box, for it was believed that the candles used in a wake would have the power to cure burns if rubbed on the skin of someone so injured.

If you visit the Hugh Rogan stone cottage today, be sure to close your eyes for a minute or two and try to visualize an Irish wake, there in front of the large stone fireplace, with the dust of centuries and memories of the past in the air.

And don't be surprised if you feel the presence of a ghost in the room with you.

Walk with Ghosts in Granville

The Jackson County town of Granville occupies one of the loveliest sites that the Cumberland River has to offer.

The high hills and rock bluffs of the Cumberland Plateau loom in the background of vibrant green farmland...called 'bottom land' by the people who live on their stretch of river.

Though small in size, Granville thinks big!

After years of dwindling population as its young people sought jobs in bigger cities or other states, and seeing its businesses shuttered and closed, the town pulled up its britches and faced the future with large dreams and dogged determination.

Beginning with the restoration of the T. B. Sutton General Store, virtually unchanged since its construction in 1880, and continuing to other buildings, the unincorporated town has literally been reborn.

New businesses occupy old storefronts and the community has established a museum recognizing its history...much of which revolved around its river location

'Quaint' is a word that comes to mind when you visit. In fact, its charm and size led it to be compared to the fictional town of Mayberry of television fame.

Grabbing onto that comparison, Granville now bills itself as 'Tennessee's Mayberry Town', complete with a Floyd's Barber Shop, a replica of Sheriff Andy Taylor's jail and an old patrol car parked on the street.

Other new attractions, include a quilt museum, a show room of antique cars, one of the largest collections of whiskey decanters in the world and gift shops that sell regional and Mayberry themed merchandise.

It now attracts visitors from across the nation as it hosts regular festivals, music shows, themed events and good food.

Every October the town's residents volunteer to conduct a 'ghost walk' down its main street... one of the only two streets in the town.

Costumed presenters tell of a tragic love between a young couple, Alexandra and Harrison.

The story, as you may have already guessed, does not have a happy ending...

It seems that Alexandra's family was of a higher social and economic status than that of her lover, Harrison. Things were further complicated by her dictatorial father, who may have done away with his wife, Alexandra's mother.

To prevent the possible marriage of his lovely only child, Alexandra's father conspires with a steamboat captain to offer Harrison a job on his boat, a job that will take him away from Granville for six long months...long enough for his daughter to forget her handsome beau.

But, the father didn't count on the young couple to faithfully exchange letters and, rather than forget each other, they are only more intense in their love. As we all know, 'absence makes the heart grow fonder'.

Complicating the story is the fact that Alexandra's father has picked out another man for her to marry. This fellow, Sterling by name, is anxious to wed the lovely Alexandra. He is also jealous of Harrison, perhaps insanely so!

At the regular stops on the ghost walk, where the volunteer presenters show off old dwellings or local points of interest, other costumed volunteers read from letters written by the ill-fated sweethearts.

Realizing that his plans were going awry, Alexandra's father arranges for young Harrison to fall overboard on the steamboat, his body disappearing into the deep dark waters of the Cumberland River.

Distraught, as we can imagine, poor Alexandra spurs the advances of Sterling, her father's choice for a husband.

One day, Sterling overhears Alexandra reading aloud one of Harrison's letters, and is consumed with anger. He grabs her by the neck and begins choking her...

Her lifeless body drops to the floor.

Since this is a ghost story, you the reader may have already guessed how the 'ghost walk' ends.

The presenter tells the assembled listeners that, to this day, the ghosts of Alexandra and Harrison may be seen...late at night as the fog rolls in off the river, holding hands as they walk along the shore.

While we haven't personally seen any ghosts at Granville, we admit that a ghost would have a difficult time finding a lovelier place to spend eternity, walking and holding hands with their ghostly lover.

Cairo, A Ghost Town on the Cumberland

For a town on the Cumberland River to be called "Cairo" is certainly unusual.

If you were to start a town from scratch as the first settlers had the opportunity to do, you would most likely name it after yourself. There are a whole passel of towns along the river named for people: Nashville, Clarksville, Gallatin, Adams, Hartsville, Donelson, Smithland and Gainesboro.

Cairo was the name chosen by General James Winchester, who served in the Continental Army and later earned his military title during the War of 1812. He was also one of the largest landholders on the frontier.

When Winchester arrived in what is now Sumner County in 1785, he was wise to the ways of making money. The general built a grist mill, owned a rock quarry for mill stones and invested in the mercantile business.

He also built a large impressive stone house for he and his family on a rock bluff overlooking a creek that flowed into the Cumberland River.

Knowing that there was money to be made in real estate, just as real estate developers of today, in 1799 he purchased 150 acres of land right on the river a few miles from his home, with the intention of building a town and selling building lots to the people who would live there.

He chose the name 'Cairo' in homage to the Egyptian city of the same name. Perhaps he envisioned a large port city for the fast growing area, as the county of Sumner had been organized in 1786.

By 1800, the town of Cairo had been laid out and building lots were being sold.

As the fledging town began to rise, stores built, houses put up and the warehouses needed to hold goods for shipping down river, General Winchester had hopes that as a thriving little town, it might be named the county seat.

Fate has little interest in the plans and hopes of mortal men.

In 1802, the town of Gallatin was laid out and its location, on the old Immigrant Trail from Knoxville to Nashville, proved more practical and it was named the seat of county government.

Yet, Cairo continued to grow and prosper.

By 1812, it could boast 12 stores, a steam powered cotton mill, a woolen mill, a still house, a sawmill, a grist mill, a blacksmith, a carpenter, a cooper and even a silversmith.

Yet, again fate had plans of her own.

Gallatin's growth was Cairo's loss.

The effects of the Civil War, the years of reconstruction and other towns having their own riverboat ports, led to the town being all but abandoned.

By 1855, a visit by a Nashville reporter noted that only one house appeared occupied.

In the early 1900's the community could only claim a church and a school for African Americans built with Rosenwald funds. About them lay the remnants of its earlier prosperity overgrown with weeds and ornamental shrubs gone untrimmed for generations.

A visitor today can still find the old building foundations if they know where to look. Less than five homes are scattered here and there. The old school and church are still standing.

You would never dream that this had once been a town with a noble name and bigger dreams... all gone.

We think of ghost towns as being something that you would find out west where once prosperous gold and silver mines brought people in by the hundreds, only to have them move on when the 'mother lode' ran out.

Those ghost towns attract tourists who pose by deserted saloons or opera houses.

Yet the Cumberland River has its own little ghost town in Cairo...a town gone, just a shadow of its former life.

If you drive the back roads of Sumner County and turn steadily south, towards the river, you will find 'Cairo Road'.

Follow it as it winds around fields and forests. Follow it to the end, where you will arrive right at the river. Now, a small boat ramp allows people to launch their fishing boats where steamboats once tied up.

The river is wider now, due to the impounded waters of Old Hickory Lake, built in the early 1950s.

Try to imagine wagons of cotton and tobacco and corn pulled by stout teams of mules. Imagine the town's old wooden stores, sidewalks and dirt streets, women in long skirts and men in tall silk hats, children running barefoot to school, buggies taking folks to church…imagine a town.

If you linger till dark, they say if you allow yourself to relax, you can close your eyes and listen…and, the evening breeze will carry sounds to you, the sounds of people talking, the distant lyrics of a hymn sung by a congregation of believers, the sounds of children skipping rocks on the water, the whistle of a steamboat, the work songs of enslaved men and women working in the fields…the noises of the past, ghostly sounds.

They are all that remain of Cairo.

The One-eyed Woman And The"Clickety, Click, Clack!"

The African American slaves of the past had their own ghost stories and superstitions.

With our country being a nation of immigrants, we know that belief in 'haunts' or 'ghosts' occurs in every ethnic background found in our country today.

So, it was that the African Americans carried to our shores due to the slave trade, brought their own unique tales of ghostly spirits and beliefs in 'conjure men', 'boohags', and 'boodaddies'.

Slave dwellings often had their doors painted blue, a color thought to have the power to ward off evil spirits.

We may laugh at this, thinking it a foolish notion, but no more foolish than keeping a rabbit's foot in your pocket or looking for a fourleaf clover!

One African belief, related to the supernatural, was the making of a bottle tree. Glass bottles, especially blue ones, would be stuck onto limbs or onto the branches of small shrubs.

Wandering spirits would see them on their nightly rambles and be mesmerized. The spirits would enter the bottles through the opening at the bottle's neck and once inside, be confused and unable to find their way out.

When the light of day arrived in the morning, it would shine on the captured spirits, turning them into dust.

A conjure man or conjure woman could 'conjure'...mix up...a potion to help a sick person, bring good fortune or perhaps make a person lucky in love.

A boohag was a witch and like the witches of other cultures, could cause harm. Boohags, despite their name, were not necessarily ugly, but could be very pretty...the better to fool an unsuspecting man into marriage.

A boodaddy was a small talisman made with a handful of swamp mud, moss and some sweet grass, shaped roughly into the form of a man...with a large head and rough body. You would have it fashioned by a conjure man and set aside to dry.

Then, keeping your boodaddy in your pocket or in a cloth bag around your neck, you were safe from the evil eye!

Despite the protection of a boodaddy, little slave children might sit by the dim light of a fireplace on a cool dark autumn night and listen to their granddaddy tell them a ghost story.

The slaves who lived on the large plantations around Lebanon, in Wilson County, would have known a story like this one, the tale of the

'clickety, click, clack'.

As the grandaddy would tell it, he would act out the actions and speak in different voices like he thought the folks in his story would.

The story he might tell was this one about an old one-eyed slave woman, too old for work, and living alone in a cabin at the edge of a large plantation.

In her youth, one eye had gotten diseased and had to be removed.

Now, in her old age, she kept to herself, not having a family of her own...just her, a few chickens and a small garden. She had nothing of any value...except, that is, for a gold coin that she valued above all else in the world.

How she came to have a single gold coin, no one knew, but had it she did.

The frailties of old age caught up with her and knowing that she was dying, she pulled the gold coin from its hiding place in the mud chinking of her log cabin.

She handed it to another slave woman and asked that it be placed on her one good eye at her death and buried with her.

The children would ask their grandaddy why she wanted a coin on her eye and he would explain.

"You see," he would tell them, "it is a common practice to place a coin on each eye of a dead person to keep their eye lids shut, because a person's eyes would be open in death."

No one wants to look at a dead person and have them staring right back at you...especially the people who would sit up all night with a dead person to watch over the body till the funeral the next day.

Her directions were followed and after she took her last breath, the kindly slave woman reached over and closed the old woman's one good eye, and placed the gold coin there.

The next day, another old slave, who was crippled and couldn't do much work in the fields, dug the grave.

The old woman was wrapped in one of her own handstitched patchwork quilts and placed in the grave.

The plantation foreman said a few words and her fellow slaves sang the plaintive words of an old spiritual. Perhaps they sang "Swing low sweet chariot, coming for to carry me home..."

After that, those gathered by the grave were sent back to work.

Only the crippled grave digger was left to fill in the grave.

Which he did.

But first, he pulled the edge of the patchwork quilt back and gazed one more time at the gold coin on the old woman's one good eye.

He had never seen such a large gold coin and he had certainly never had something so valuable in his pockets.

"What a shame," he said to himself, "for that shiny gold coin to be buried with this old woman...no use to her now!"

And, just like that, he picked it from off her good eye and put it in his pocket.

Then the granddaddy would be sure to tell his wide-eyed grandchildren, that when the crippled old grave digger reached back to put the quilt over her face again, her one good eyelid was now open and she seemed to be staring right at him.

"What do you reckon she saw?" he asked them.

They probably squealed with delight guessing that she saw who took her gold coin.

The old gravedigger put the quilt back over her face and grabbed the shovel he had used to dig the grave and began to fill the grave back up.

That should be the end of the story...but, it isn't.

When night came, before climbing into his bed, he looked at that bright gold coin again. It sure was mighty fine.

He placed it into a little tin snuff box and placed it in a small old wooden trunk that he kept under his rickety old bed. "It will be safe there," he thought to himself as he pushed the wooden trunk back under his bed.

The stub of a candle burned on a little table in the center of the room and he blew it out and getting into bed, he pulled the covers up about his shoulders for the night was a little cool.

All was quiet until the moon went behind a cloud right about midnight, the witching hour, when haunts begin their nightly prowling.

It was then that the old man woke up to the sound of footsteps on the small porch of his cabin.

"Was he just hearing things?" the granddaddy would ask.

The children would look at each other and lean closer to him so as to not miss a word of his story as he continued.

Then the footsteps seemed to be walking across the floor of the cabin, though the door was barred with a piece of rusty old iron.

It was too dark in the one room cabin to see anything, but that didn't matter because the old man wasn't looking...he was hiding under the blanket on his bed!

Suddenly the poor fellow heard a most distressing noise...it sounded like this, 'Clickety, click, clack'.

It was the sound of the gold coin trying to get out of the little tin snuff box.

As if that wasn't scary enough for the old man, he then heard a woman's voice, an old woman's voice. Low and slow, he heard the voice utter, "Is that my gold coin talking to me?" That was too much for the old man.

He jerked the blankets off and grabbed the candle stub and a match from his little table.

He lit the candle and in the feeble light it gave off, he looked around the room.

There was no one there but him.

He quickly pulled the wooden trunk out from under his bed.

Opening it up, he saw the little tin snuff box. It was right where he had placed it and when he opened it up, the shiny gold coin shone brightly back at him.

"Had he been dreaming?" the grandaddy would ask and the children would all say, "No!" and he would continue his story.

The old grave digger stared at that coin for a long time... you see, it had him in its grasp.

He closed the tin box and put it back in the wooden trunk and closed the lid and pushed it back under the bed.

Before he blew out the candle, he walked to the door to make sure it was still barred with the rusty old piece of iron.

It was.

So, relieved, he blew out the candle and returned to his bed, straightened out his blanket and pulled it up about his shoulders.

But, no sooner had he pulled the blanket up than he heard the soft tread of footsteps in his room.

Then loud and clearly, he heard, “Clickety, click, clack...clickety, click, clack!”

“Is that my gold coin talking to me” came a sad old voice...only this time the voice seemed to be right beside the old man’s bed!

He sat straight up and hollered, “Go away woman! You don’t need that old coin!”

The children would likely jump back when the granddaddy spoke those words, just like the frightened old man would have.

The room of the old log cabin got quiet...deadly quiet.

Then, there was the sound again, “Clickity, click, clack...clickity, click, clack...clickity, click, clack...”

Jumping out of his bed, the old man lit the candle again and looked around the room, then pulled the wooden trunk out from under the bed.

He opened it up again. He saw the tin snuff box there and he peeked inside...yes, the gold coin was still there and it seemed to be smiling at him!

Shaking like a leaf on a briar bush in a windstorm, the old man pulled his raggedy old pants on and then his shoes. He pushed the little tin snuff box deep in his pocket and rushed over to the door.

It didn't take him a half minute to unbar the door, grab the shovel from its place on the porch and start down the road lickety-split, headed to that old woman's grave.

"Well, I don't need to tell you the rest of the story," the old granddaddy would say, but the children insisted he tell more...

The old man dug that grave back open and placed that gold coin back on the old woman's only good eye, closing her eye lid first, then pulling the quilt back over her face.

By the time the dirt was back in place on that grave, the sun was at the edge of the horizon.

Tired and with a little limp, he struggled up the stairs to his cabin, closed the door behind him and pulled off his muddy shoes and old raggedy pants and climbed onto the bed.

Wrapping the blanket about him, he closed his eyes and fell right to sleep and it was a good long deep sleep because there would be no more footsteps, no more voices and no more,

"Clickety, click, clack!"

Crowfoot, the Roustabout

The Cumberland River was the highway of the Native Americans, the early settlers and the merchants and travelers of the mid to late 1800's. If, for instance, you wanted to go from Celina or Granville to Nashville or any point west of that city...you traveled on the river!

From the wood canoes of the Cherokee, the Shawnee and the Creek Indians, to the flat bottomed boats of the pioneers, to the wood palaces we call 'showboats', the river was the means of transportation.

Steamboats were the crowning achievement of the men who designed river boats.

A steamboat was powered by a wood fired boiler that created the steam power to turn the big paddlewheel to move the boat up and down the river. The boat would have two decks and a wheelhouse on top of that.

The lower level was usually reserved for hauling livestock to market.

In the fall season, the lower level would be used for large hogshead barrels of tobacco, or sacks of corn to be used to make corn liquor. Cotton was shipped to markets in Memphis and New Orleans. Lumber and building materials were shipped both up and down the river.

When the small general stores in the river towns needed goods to sell, they arrived by steamboat.

Every river town had a 'landing' where a boat could pull up and unload. The landing would have a warehouse to store the boxes and barrels of merchandise...always built well above the flood stage of the river!

Upriver from Nashville, smaller steam powered boats were used...'packets' they were called.

Because the further you went up river, the shallower the water was, a packet steamer had a smaller 'draft', or amount of keel below the water line. That way, the packet could travel all the way up river...unless it was a dry spell and then the water depth above Granville would keep boats from going further upriver until a good rain made the river run higher.

It took real men to run a steamboat, from the 'pilot' who had to know every bend in the river and where the sandbars were, to the men who loaded and unloaded the huge bales of cotton or loaded the firewood needed to keep the fire going for the boiler.

We have lots of stories about the men who worked on the river.

They were called 'roustabouts' and they were usually a rough lot.

The work was hard, the pay little and the demands of the job miserable.

But, there was always a class of men who would take the work and they often drank a little to cut the chill of the night air or to help them forget the long hours and back breaking work.

The familiarity of the job made the roustabouts call each other by their first names or, often enough, some sort of nickname based on a physical trait or a peculiar habit or a play on their given name.

Every boat had a 'Red' or a 'Preacher' or a 'Moe'.

The roustabout in our story was nicknamed 'Crowfoot'.

There were worse names, some we can't repeat in polite society.

Crowfoot worked the stretch of river above Nashville, traveling once a week from the capital city to Burkesville, Kentucky, and back, when the water was deep enough.

On one such trip, it was dark and the air wet with sweat and mist from the river. Crowfoot had gotten hold of a bottle of cheap whisky...or maybe a jug of moonshine. In either case, he was bordering on being all out drunk...and his tongue and temper showed it.

He got into a battle of words with the Captain's Mate, the man who told the roustabouts what to do.

Face to face the two men glared at each other till one of them tried to push the other aside and a scuffle began.

With his equilibrium off due to the liquor, Crowfoot lost his balance and fell towards the railing. The Captain's Mate then kicked at him, causing him to fall overboard.

The boat was going at a pretty good clip and the Captain's Mate decided to let Crowfoot stay in the water rather than holler "Man overboard" or make any effort to cause the boat to stop and rescue the drunken roustabout. Maybe, he felt that the cold water would cool off Crowfoot's anger and he could swim to shore and wait there till he was sober and could flag down a ride on another steam packet.

As the story goes, as the other roustabouts and the Captain's Mate looked back, they never saw Crowfoot come back up to the surface of the river. The dark deep river seemed to have just swallowed him up.

If the men on the boat were superstitious or were worried about their fellow roustabout, we don't know. The simple truth is that they never saw ole Crowfoot again.

But we do know that a few months later...something happened.

Once again on its weekly trip upriver and back, as the steam powered vessel passed Carthage and then the community of Rome, headed toward Hartsville and Gallatin, it was once again a dark night, the air damp and there was another drunken man on board.

This time it was the Captain's Mate who was unsteady on his feet.

Reading from a newspaper account of the incident, just as it was written "...when the boat reached the approximate point where Crowfoot had been kicked into the river, a weird thing happened. Passengers on the Texas deck screamed, roustabouts covered their eyes, and even the Captain gaped in open-mouthed amazement as a black swirling mass swept down out of the starlit sky and shoved the mate into the swirling waters of the Cumberland. His screams were stifled in the foam as the boat sped past him, and the last anybody saw of the mate was a hand waving pathetically for help as it sank beneath the surface of the water." According to the story, the Captain tried to stop the boat and turn around to rescue the poor man...but, the steam packet refused to obey and continued to race down the river...just the way it had done when poor Crowfoot fell overboard.

If it was the ghost of Crowfoot that pushed the Captain's Mate into the cold waters, seeking revenge, we can't say...but, it sure looks that way!

"That's Just Bob..."

This ghost is that of a child, a little boy.

Ghost stories often involve a child, a child who died young and it is their fate to stay that way.

They may haunt the stairways or halls of old homes or linger around the stones of a small family cemetery playing all alone.

The old Corley Cemetery, just over the hill from the Cumberland River as it flows between Hartsville and Lebanon, has a ghostly child. Families that lived by the cemetery would say that they would sometimes look towards the small graveyard and see a little boy among the old tombstones, playing hide-n-seek or some other childhood game.

They knew he was a ghost because if they tried to walk over to the cemetery for a closer look, by the time they got there, he would always be gone.

The little boy in this story lived on the Caney Fork, which flows into the Cumberland close to the town of Carthage.

Walton's Ferry stood close to that junction and is rich in history in its own right, as many a pioneer used the ferry to cross the river there, until a bridge was built.

The child in this story was named Robert, but that is a big name for a small child and it didn't take long for people to just call him "Bob", so Bob he was.

An old road ran by the house where Bob lived and, as can be imagined, the young boy was mesmerized by the teams of mules or oxen that pulled the big wagons up and down the road, straining on the hill close by the house.

Back in the old days, many a young man took their first job as a teamster or drover on the old road, hiring out to help drive a wagon of corn or lumber northward to Kentucky, just up the way from the banks of the Caney Fork.

The trip took several days back then, the road turning and twisting and going up and down with the many hills on the way.

The boys would load and unload the big wagons, camping at night beside the road, caring for the livestock and rolling up in an old blanket under the wagon at night to keep the morning dew off.

Bob's pappy or maybe it was his grandpappy, took some scraps of wood and his whittling knife and made little Bob a wagon of his own, one he could play with, out in the yard, close to the old road.

He would spend hours in the dirt, loading and unloading the handmade little wagon with gravel or sticks, whatever he might find. If he was missing, all the family had to do was look out the door on the porch and there he would be, playing with his wagon beside the road.

Bob loved watching the older boys, waving to them as they passed by. He had the envy that all little boys have towards the bigger boys, "When

I grow up, I'm gonna be just like them," he would say.

Fate had other plans.

Little Bob took sick and medicine not being what it is today, he lay on his bed slowly slipping away.

Perhaps his mother or dad said something to keep Bob in good spirits, to make him smile despite his worsening condition.

"Hey, Bob," we can imagine his pappy saying, "when you get better, you can play with your wagon out there by the road, and wave to the fellers on the big trucks...as the big wagons were sometimes called...and they'll wave back to you!"

"Won't that be fine!" his mama would say.

"Yeah," he would answer," and one day it will be me a sittin' up there on the big seat on one of them big old trucks...pullin' the big hill..."

But, his voice would get fainter as the hours went by and before long he had passed away.

They say his coffin was the smallest most of the family or neighbors had ever seen and how sad it was to place his little wagon beside him before they slowly closed the lid.

The cemetery lay close to the road...and, that's part of our story.

You see, for years after that, people walking up the Old Kentucky Road, up the big hill, would swear that they heard the sounds of a big team a haulin' up the hill, but there was no team in sight.

It was more than one person who heard the noises.

They would clearly hear the turning of the big wheels on the gravel of the road, the teamster hollering to his mules, and the creaking of the stout wagons as they moved.

It was a mystery to someone who wasn't from the community, but it wasn't a mystery to the few folks who lived there.

The people in the neighborhood knew where the sound came from, and they would tell each other, "It's just Bob and his trucks going up the road!"

We can guess that was a better explanation that saying to someone, "Why, you must be crazy!"

The old road is gone now, replaced with a modern paved highway, one that loops around the big hill and is level and straight. So, people no longer hear Bob and his little wagon.

We like to think, that if Bob's spirit lingers still, that he can look down from his grave in the family cemetery and watch traffic go by on the blacktop road below. And, we know for certain, that little Bob would like to be at the steering wheel of one of those big ole' eighteen wheelers!

Doctor Donoho's Story

If you were to stretch the Cumberland River out into a straight line it would go through more that the states of Tennessee and Kentucky!

The river's six hundred and eighty-eight miles turn and twist and bend and twist again, never in a straight line as it wanders from the hills around Burkesville, Kentucky, through Tennessee and then back into Kentucky before it runs into the Ohio River at Smithland, Kentucky.

Those bends along the river have names, such as Beasley's Bend, or Neeley's Bend, named after pioneer families. One bend is named for its shape, Horseshoe Bend!

In this story of ghostly encounters, we visit Puryear's Bend, which is also named for an early family. According to family tradition, the Puryear family was traveling downstream on a flatboat when a member of the family got sick.

Others on the boat were afraid that the illness might be the deadly smallpox and insisted that the boat pull over to shore and let the sick person off the boat...which is exactly what happened.

The ill individual got off, but the rest of their family refused to leave them there alone on the wooded shore and joined them on the banks of the bend in the river.

That person survived whatever illness they had and the family was pleased with their surroundings and ended up making that spot their home, the big bend in the river taking their name.

Years later, the doctor of the closest town, Hartsville, was called one night to tend to another sick person.

It was "old" Doctor Donoho, as to be distinguished from his son, "young" Doctor Donoho, who answered the call.

This is his story, as he told it and as it has been repeated over the years:

"Now, I'm not a superstitious man.

Well, I might throw a little salt over my shoulder if I spill some at the supper table. It's bad luck to spill the salt shaker they say. But, I do that lightheartedly. The kids always get a kick out of it.

And, I always change my way into town if a black cat crosses my path. I just cross the street and walk on the other side, as if nothing had happened. But, I do that because my dad always did and well, I guess it's a habit.

But, I've never been one to believe in ghosts...or 'haints' as people here abouts call 'em.

I've had people tell me they've seen ghosts, but I don't hold much cotton with such tales. Maybe they had a little too much corn liquor or maybe they saw something else and thought it was a ghost.

Had a fellow tell me once, "Doc I done seen a 'haint'. Sure as I am sittin' here!" But, that old man was given to tall tales so I didn't pay him much mind.

Saw an owl one evening myself. Flew right by my head, not five feet away from me. They fly quiet like you know. If I was the superstitious type I might have sworn it was a ghost that flew by my head...if it had been dark and I was going by a graveyard.

Yes, like I said, I'm not the superstitious type.

But, all that changed one night.

I'd been called in the middle of supper to tend to an old woman out in the 'bend', Puryear's Bend that is.

She was purt old, close to ninety. Lived with her youngest son and his family. They cherished the old lady and were upset that she might be dying, so they had sent one of the boys to town on the family mule and he had rode it straight to the house.

I told him to go on back home and I'd hurry with my supper and be along directly. I knew how to get there.

When I left the house, I was sure I wouldn't be gittin' back before dark, so I told the Missus to leave the porch lantern lit for me.

Well, there's not much to tell. I got there and the old lady was sure enough dying. Just wore out from living. But, she took it gracefully and died with a small Bible clutched to her chest.

The son immediately stepped into the front parlor and stopped the family clock, then his wife and oldest daughter took linens and covered up all the mirrors in the house. They were superstitious that way.

They offered me a bed, since it was after midnight, if I wanted to wait and go back to town in the morning. I respectfully declined, telling 'em I slept best in my own bed.

If I had known what was to happen next, I would have taken them up on that offer!

As it was, I got back on my mare, old 'Kate', and turned her towards town. She knew the way. Many's the time I just turned old Kate to face home and let her go while I half dozed in the saddle knowing she would get me home safe and sound.

There's only one road into the 'bend'. One way in and one way out. The road is kind of twisty with a few hills and low places where the fog gathers on cool nights.

I hadn't gone far when we turned a curve in the road and the moon showed up right big, casting its light on the old dead sycamore tree that stood right beside the road. I knew the tree well 'cause it was where a man had been hung for barn burning. The tree died not long after that 'cause, as the locals all tell it, "If'en you hang a man from a tree it puts a curse on that there tree and it will up 'n die!"

Course, it was a dry summer after that hanging, following a dry spring and that old sycamore...they like their roots wet, you know... it just died naturally. Yet, the people in the 'bend' are superstitious and they blamed the tree's dying on the hanging. But, me, I'm not the superstitious type.

It was 'bout then that the old full moon went behind a cloud.

I pulled my suit jacket a little tighter around my neck as I suddenly felt a chill in the air and old Kate gave a curious toss of her head, as if her bit were a little too tight.

And, it was then that I felt it!

I could'a swore that someone...or something...had just hopped right up on the horse and was sittin' right behind me!

The kids often ride behind their daddy when I take a short ride, otherwise I hitch up the buggy. So, I know what it feels like to have someone behind me on a horse. Why, my brother and I used to piggyback ride down to the 'granny hole' to go swimmin' back when we were youngun's.

Yep, I know when someone is sitting behind me on a horse!

I turned in the saddle to see who it was, thinking someone was playing a joke on me.

It was then I saw the fellow...I'm not sayin' it was a ghost. It looked just like an ordinary man. It wasn't anyone I knew and suddenly the thought of a robber came to me and I swung my arm to knock him off.

But my arm just passed right through him!

I kept swinging and he kept sitting!

I guess all my commotion, and I may have been doing some shouting, made old Kate kick up her heels and start to running.

We must have been a sight, if anybody had been around to watch. Me, a shouting and hollering, old Kate a going faster and faster, and me a swinging at that man and him just a sittin' there.

We got to a spot on the road, close to the old Winn place, right by that old cemetery belonging to their family, when the moon came out from behind that cloud and that man disappeared, just as fast as he had appeared in the first place.

I don't mind telling' you that I kept that old mare at a fast pace all the way into town. I didn't slow up till I saw my porch light on in the distance.

Like I say, I'm not the superstitious type and I'm not gonna swear I saw a ghost or a haint, but I will tell you this. I've never gone back to the 'bend' to doctor anyone if I know I have to travel that road after dark...they'll just have to wait till daylight!"

Moonshine and Ghosts

There is an old saying about the early pioneers of Tennessee and Kentucky. It goes like this, “The English would build a church; the Germans would build a barn; and the Irish would build a whiskey still.”

Whiskey!

The word itself is Irish and the people of old Erin call whiskey, ‘the water of life’.

Admittedly, every culture has found a way to ferment nature’s bounty and distill some sort of alcoholic beverage. Yet, we give the Irish a lot of credit for their mastery of the golden hued beverage so well associated with them.

Long ago, in the hills of Scotland where they also made whiskey, to keep from paying taxes, the common folk found that they could work their stills late at night to avoid being seen...hence, the nickname ‘moonshine’.

The English authorities, in an effort to get the troublesome Scots out of their hair, offered the Scots low rent on farm land...if they would just move to Ireland.

Many did so, and with time a group of people evolved that we call ‘Scots-Irish’. When those Scots-Irish immigrated to the American colonies, they found that the English, whom both the Scots and the Irish harbored a hatred for, had all of the good land taken.

The poor Scots-Irish were pushed down the coast of America to the Carolinas and hence to what would become Kentucky and Tennessee.

Once there, they found that the many cool mountain springs lent themselves to making good whiskey...often attributed to the water having passed through layers of the native limestone.

You might not associate ghosts with stills for making whiskey, but many an inebriated man has claimed to have seen a ghost.

This ghost story makes the rounds in Jackson County, Tennessee, an area drained by the Cumberland River, being passed along from one generation to the next.

Back in the days of log cabins and dirt roads, of travel by horse and wagon, of young men working on their parent's farms, Saturdays were something to look forward to.

Of course, on a farm, Saturdays were just as full of activity as any other day of the week, but because the next day was Sunday, people would often stop work a little earlier on Saturday and relax a little. It was time for the small pleasures of rural living, when someone with a fiddle would entertain the neighbors at a barn dance or the one room school would have a box supper.

While the older folks visited, the young unmarried men would kind of congregate together and talk mules, how tall the corn was and which gals were the prettiest.

Afterwards, those young men might decide to visit the nearest whiskey still for a 'snort' before they headed on home, knowing that they would have to get up on Sunday and go to church with the family and on Monday start all over again.

You can be sure that the fellows knew where a jug of moonshine could be had, just as they knew where the best fishing hole was.

Yes, sometimes these frisky lads would have a little too much and get to acting foolish, singing out loud, racing their mules down the dirt roads lickety-split and pulling pranks on their neighbors.

The next morning in church, they would sit there listening to the preacher, all bleary-eyed and suffering a hangover.

One such group of young men had gained a reputation for their foolishness and lectures from their parents and sermons on the evils of alcohol didn't seem to have much effect.

But, then something happened.

As the boys were sitting around drinking one Saturday night, one of them saw a ghost!

Well, with the strength of what they were drinking, that should come as no surprise!

One Tennessee moonshiner made his brew so stout that he told people, "You better be standing on level ground when you take a swaller!"

They probably saw cows fly too!

But, when the story got around, the local Methodist Circuit Rider saw an opportunity to 'scare' the men into sobriety.

He decided to dress up in a white sheet and spook the boys good, since he knew that there really were no such things as ghosts.

Asking around he was told where the boys would gather to drink their moonshine after visiting the nearest still. And, when the next Saturday night arrived, he had his white bed sheet and his routine all worked out, "If you boys don't stop a drinking, you'll end up a ghost like me. Can't go to heaven and afraid of hell!"

As expected, the young men arrived at the still after dark, having left early from a quilting party. They pulled out their quarters and nickels and pennies till they had enough to pay the old moonshiner for a gallon jug of the potent brew.

Then they ambled down the holler a bit to a flat spot by the creek, tied up their mules and sat down on a fallen tree trunk. They started passing the jug around.

The preacher, not much older than the boys he was getting ready to scare, lay hidden behind a rock fence opposite the log where they were sitting.

He waited till they had all had a few sips, enough to loosen their tongues and get them to laughing and acting silly.

Suddenly, the drinking boys heard an eerie wail, "Whoooooo!"

They turned in unison to see the pastor slowly rise up from behind the rock fence.

"Whoooooo!"

"Lord, have mercy!" one of them cried, "It's a haint!"

"Whoooooo!" The preacher moaned again, about ready to deliver his rehearsed lines.

"Sweet Jesus, save us!" another one yelled.

Then, as our preacher began to sway back and forth and to raise his arms, another voice rang out...

"Lookie, thar's two of em!"

Hearing this, the preacher looked to his side and there was indeed another figure in white hanging in the moonlight, right beside him!

We don't need to tell you what happened next...

That preacher man out ran those boys down the road!

The Church Window

One wouldn't think a stained glass window in a church would harbor a ghostly tale, but that is the case in this story.

While we once again hesitate to name the exact church and location to keep curiosity seekers away and avoid people taking pictures during services, we will say that the church in question lies just a few miles from the banks of the Cumberland River.

In fact, the church sits on the appropriately named 'River Street' of one of the many small towns that grew up along the river, owing much of its growth to the shipping of local produce, tobacco and such down river to markets.

The church began services before 1810, making it one of the oldest churches in the town.

Over the years, it out grew its first building and the current structure, the one in our story, was built following World War II.

It is a trim structure, well maintained, reflecting the pride that a congregation has in its place of worship.

In the more recent 1980's, there was a desire to fill the church's gothic style windows with stained glass, a considerable expense for the number of windows in the sanctuary.

A drive to have individual families 'sponsor' a window worked and the windows were ordered from a reputable company. Each window would have a small scene from a Bible story in a circle in the middle, with a verse from the scriptures at the bottom...chosen by the family...and the family's name, in recognition of their monetary contribution.

There was no preference about location, and that was left to the installers...which is when our ghost makes his appearance.

Considerable preparations had to made to accommodate the new windows, since the older ones had to be removed, and new casing put in before the new vibrant colored glass windows were installed.

One lady of the church in particular was involved in the project and she routinely stopped by the building as the work began and kept an eye on the process. Her name was Eleanor.

The workers were experts in their field and came from West Virginia to install the windows. They quickly developed a rapport with Eleanor.

On the day the first window was installed, Eleanor happened to drive by and seeing the progress immediately stopped and went inside to see for herself.

The first window shown beautifully as the day's sunlight lit up its jewel toned glass.

The scene from the Bible was impressive, the verse from scripture showed up dramatically, and the family name "Hardy" was easily read.

Although she, as the church's representative, didn't question why the Hardy family window was the first one installed and, coincidentally, the one closest to the pulpit, until a workmen casually mentioned, “Mr. Hardy came by to tell us where he wanted his window.”

Eleanor gave the men a look of surprise, as Mr. Hardy had been dead for several years and the window was a memorial paid for by a descendant who did not live in the town, but many miles away.

She responded by saying, “Well, that is interesting as Mr. Hardy is dead and has been for quite some time!”

Yet, the men insisted that a Mr. Hardy had entered the building, and he had told them where he wanted his window placed.

Eleanor grilled the men as a detective would and asked them to describe the individual who had walked into the sanctuary as they worked.

She was old enough to remember Mr. Hardy and their description fit the elderly man to a ‘t”.

A little embarrassed by the situation, the head workman asked her, “What should we do?”

Without any hesitation, Eleanor said, “Do what Mr. Hardy told you! After all, if a man goes to the trouble to return from the dead, I guess you had better do as he says!”

According to the newspaper write up following the dedication of the new windows, attempts to identify the man who walked in to give the workers directions had not been identified, contacts with the family insisting that not one of the descendants had made any such demands nor had visited the town during the installation.

We leave you to decide for yourself if our Mr. Hardy was a ghost!

Not Now, Miss Nonnie!

The old town of Damascus, Tennessee, was settled before Tennessee became a state, right there on the banks of Little Goose Creek, which flows a few miles further till it empties into the Cumberland River.

The little community began when a grist mill was placed on a narrow part of the creek, a few miles above where it flowed into the Cumberland River. Today, it has been incorporated into the newer, but larger, town of Hartsville. One of the first homes built in Damascus was a simple two story log structure, still standing today, where the owners ran a tannery...a place to process animal skins into tanned leather.

In later years the house was added onto and doubled in size.

It is not often that I have been invited into a home that acclaims a ghost resides there, but when I first moved to Hartsville that was the case.

The family was proud of their old home and its history.

And, as I sat on a chair in the living room, the history that they shared with me was indeed something to talk about.

The home's elderly couple told me how the house stood on the old Immigrant Trail, the first road to connect Nashville to Knoxville and how during the Civil War, soldiers from both North and South had ridden through the front yard on their way to battle.

In the late 1870's, the same family that had added onto the home suffered a great tragedy, I was told.

They were prosperous and well thought of in town.

There had been several daughters, two of whom died before their eighteenth birthdays. Another was married and had started a family. The last daughter continued to live at home, taking over the domestic chores after her mother's death and looking after her father and younger brother, the only son in the family.

However, the young man had gotten into the habit of going into town on weekends and enjoying a few drinks with the other young fellows in Hartsville and perhaps playing a few games of poker.

One weekend, the cards were in the young man's favor and he won the small pile of money laying on the table. Content with his success, he bid his friends goodbye and got on his horse to ride the short distance to the family home.

He never arrived!

In the morning light, his body was found lying in a ditch...his skull crushed in and his pockets empty.

There would be accusations and a suspect was charged with the killing and there would be a trial, but that has little bearing on our story.

The sister, nicknamed "Nonnie", was grief stricken.

After the funeral, she went upstairs to her room and rarely went out in public again.

For years, she sat silently in a chair in front of a window and looked mournfully out...perhaps hoping that it was all just a bad dream and that her beloved brother would come riding up to the house once more.

That was all years ago, my hosts told me.

But, it wasn't the last of Miss Nonnie.

The present owners of the home had done considerable remodeling when they got the old place and had two young daughters running through the home and about the yard.

And, as they settled into the home there would be times the sounds of footsteps could be heard upstairs...despite the fact the family was gathered downstairs.

The girls, who were now using Miss Nonnie's old bedroom, told their parents that they would wake up in the morning to find that someone had pulled up their bed covers in the night, up around their shoulders so they wouldn't get cold.

The lady of the family didn't pay much attention to what the girls said, nor to the occasional strange noise...old houses pop and crack, you know.

Then, one evening one of the girls had trouble sleeping and called down to her mother, who checked on her and to help her get to sleep, lay down on the bed next to her.

About the time that her daughter passed slowly off to slumber, the mother heard footsteps enter the room.

She looked about, wondering if her husband had come to check on them...but, there was no one in the room besides her and the two sleeping girls.

After getting up out of the bed and turning on a light, the mother looked around...even glancing under each bed.

As we sat there in the living room of the quaint old home, she told me, "now, I don't believe in ghosts and I'm not afraid of the Devil...but!"

For several more nights, the scenario was repeated.

And, each time, when the mother sat up and looked around, there was no one there.

Even someone who is not scared of the devil can only tolerate so much...something had to be done!

When another night arrived with the youngest daughter requesting her mother lay down with her, things would be different.

Prepared to end things one way or another, the mother listened patiently for the sound of footsteps and when she heard them, she said out loud in a firm voice, "No, no, Miss

Nonnie...please, not tonight!"

The sound of footsteps stopped.

And, they didn't come back.

It took, the lady of the house informed me, several times for her to admonish Miss Nonnie, but the footsteps eventually stopped altogether. The daughter stopped asking for her mother to come lay beside her and...we are led to believe...Miss Nonnie got the hint!

As a friend of the family, I have visited the home on many occasions and when I ask about Miss Nonnie, I am told that she keeps to herself nowadays and the house is quiet at night...except for the occasional creaking and popping that a two hundred year old home makes from time to time.

The Ghostly Cat at Cragfont Mansion

No collection of ghostly tales would be complete without at least one tale that involves a cat!

This tale from the Winchester family does just that.

James Winchester was a veteran of the American Revolution and fought in the War of 1812, attaining the rank of General!

He was also one of the first men on the frontier, arriving in what is now the small community of Castalian Springs, by 1785...there were still hostile Native Americans in the area.

James built a large home on a bluff overlooking a spring of his own...the spring flows into Bledsoe Creek...the creek flows a short distance into the Cumberland River.

The home is called 'Cragfont', a French spelling for the bluff, or crag, that the house faced.

Like the rocky bluff, the house is built of limestone. It is little wonder that it is still standing, over two hundred years after workmen finished its construction in 1802.

Today it is a State Historic Site and open to the public.

The original property was hundreds of acres and to farm it, General Winchester had many slaves...our story also concerns a slave.

One of the older enslaved women was known for her ability to mix up a dose of remedy for the other slaves from time to time. Even members of the Winchester family had faith in the old woman's ability to stir together some herbs and roots and add a little corn liquor to make a good cough remedy.

She was also known to do a little fortune telling and could always make a charm to protect you from whatever you were scared of...maybe something that goes 'bump' in the night.

If you were frightened of the dark, she might tie up a small bundle of dried leaves, along with a bone from a dead man's finger and then mumble a few words over them. After you gave her a small coin or promised her a piece of ginger cake and a cup of cider, she would hand it over to you.

A woman like that could be expected to have a cat...an ornery cat at that!

As the story has been handed down through the Winchester family and its descendants, a member of the Satterwhite family was visiting the Winchesters and saw a large cat stalking a turkey right there in the yard of the house. The turkey was part of a small flock being fed and fattened up for the holidays.

One of the Winchester ladies commented on the old cat, saying that it had managed to run off with several of the family's chickens and their flock had suffered as a result.

The gentleman visitor offered to 'take care of that cat', but the Winchester lady cautioned against that because, "that cat belongs to

Bessie...and Bessie practically runs this place!"

"We can't afford to make Bessie mad...we all owe so much to her in one way or another."

The debt to Bessie was enormous... who would they go to for their upset stomach, sore tooth or bunion? Not to mention the occasional charm against the evil eye or imagined ghost.

But the Satterwhite guest wasn't the least bit impressed with whatever power old Bessie might have and quickly grabbled up a burlap sack from the kitchen and just as quickly picked up the old cat and stuffed it inside the sack.

He then picked up a few stones to weight the sack down with and marched to the edge of the yard and heaved the sack, cat and all, over the edge of the rock bluff that gave the house its name.

That, it was assumed, would take care of the troublesome cat...although who was going to tell Bessie what had happened to her cat was still to be reckoned with.

Two days later, the Satterwhite visitor returned to the home to chat again.

As he sat on the rock front steps of the impressive house and visited with the Winchester ladies, they heard a noise. Looking to the direction of the commotion, they saw the old cat emerge wailing from the tall grass and head towards them.

One of the Winchester women, having witnessed the cat's supposed demise, screamed and had a fit!

She was convinced the cat had returned from the dead...what else would you expect from a cat owned by their Bessie?

The other ladies had to take her to the home of her sister who lived a short distance away, where she finally calmed down.

So, are we to believe the cat had drowned after being thrown into the creek below the rock bluff and was this just one of its proverbial nine lives that all cats are said to have?

Can cats swim?

Did the burlap sack not reach the water below and instead, get snagged on a branch of a small bush clinging to the rock bluff and then spend two days clawing its way out?

We'll never know.

Bessie was no doubt glad to see her cat again and life returned to normal, with the exception that everyone gave that old cat a little more respect and the family didn't seem to mind if an occasional chicken went missing.

The Garden at the Hermitage

The Garden at the Hermitage

Perhaps, there is no more recognized historic home in the whole state of Tennessee than that of Andrew Jackson's 'Hermitage'.

But then, the man himself is perhaps the state's best known resident!

From his humble birth in the Carolinas and being orphaned at an early age, young Andy had a hard scrabble childhood. A scar on his head from the sword of a British soldier only adds to his persona.

Yet, his years as a lawyer, politician, soldier, and president all revolve around his beloved Tennessee home...and, his beloved wife Rachel.

In 1804, Jackson purchased a large swath of land, just two miles from the banks of the Cumberland River and about twenty miles from downtown Nashville. The estate would eventually amount to just over 1,000 acres.

The fine home we see today when visiting the historic property was not built until the early 1820's.

Before that Andrew and Rachel lived in a log home, also still standing and on the self-guided tour for visitors.

We won't delve into the controversies surrounding Andrew and Rachel's romance, but we will simply acknowledge that Andrew's political opponents tried to make it look disreputable.

All of this put a heavy burden on Rachel's health and she passed away between his 1828 election as the seventh President of the United States and his swearing in, which took place in Washington, D.C. in 1829.

When the present home was built, a large garden was laid out, only a few feet from the east side of the house. There, Rachel was able to indulge in her love for flowers. Before passing away, she told her husband that she wished to be buried there, surrounded by the rows of sweet smelling perennial shrubs and flowers she had planted...but, also close to him and the home they shared.

A fire in 1831 forced a major rebuilding of most of the house and at that time, Jackson had an impressive limestone pavilion built over her grave, with columns and a copper roof. After his presidency and his return home, it is said that every evening he took a stroll through the garden, pausing at Rachel's tomb.

He would be buried beside her in 1845.

There are others buried in that corner of the garden, including the couple's adopted Native American son, Lyncoya, who died at age 17.

Despite their great love for each other, the Jacksons had no children of their own, and also adopted one of Rachel's nephews and a greatnephew.

One African American is buried there, Uncle Alfred, who was born on the estate around 1812 and was close to the family. Uncle Alfred's humble log home stood just behind the mansion. It too is open for visitors to see. Uncle Alfred's devotion to the property...he worked there up to his death in 1901...led to his funeral being held in the house and he was buried in the garden, close to the General and Rachel.

After the president's death and the Civil War, the large plantation fell on hard times.

It was in danger of being allowed to just fall down, when in 1889 it was taken over by the Ladies' Hermitage Association, a group of Tennessee women who banded together to save it after its years of neglect.

At that time the estate was being considered as the location for an old soldier's home. Tennessee had many former Confederate soldiers who were old and in poor health or were unable to financially take care of themselves. The State Legislature decided that the large estate would be a good place to build such a home.

It was built, but the Legislature deeded the president's home and about thirty acres to the women. Their organization still maintains the home today.

The sorrow the Jacksons' shared in their lifetimes could easily inspire a ghostly presence on the Hermitage property but there were other reasons for the frightening events and strange noises that people report.

In addition to Uncle Alfred, the estate was home to many slaves, who are also buried there. Their daily toils and bondage might have tempted anyone of them to linger close by, even after death.

While the home for old soldiers was in use, 480 of the men were buried on the property. The home was eventually torn down, but their graves remain. How many of those men have stayed around to frighten visitors and staff?

People who have worked at the Hermitage tell of strange noises, unexplained noises!

Two women who spent a night in the house claim to have heard what sounded like a large horse being ridden down the hallway...in the middle of the night!

Someone whistling when there was no one else in the house was reported by another worker in the home.

In the lovely old garden, where iris, buttercups and vintage peonies bloom, people hear approaching footsteps on the gravel pathways, but there is no one there. And, visitors claim to have seen the garden gate swing open, untouched by human hands.

The distinct smell of a cigar being smoked has been noticed!

Jackson was known for his fondness of a good cigar...and, Rachel is said to have smoked a pipe and the occasional cigar! Are their spirits enjoying a smoke in the afterlife, as they drift around the garden?

And, guides on the property say they have seen the ghostly forms of men in uniform...Confederate uniforms!

So far, these apparitions and noises have done no harm, other than the slight chill going down someone's back and a quickening of the pulse! But, as one of Tennessee's most popular attractions, the occasional ghost makes it all the more interesting to visit!

Tragedy at the Maxwell House Hotel

The muddy waters of the Cumberland River pass through Tennessee's capital city of Nashville, lapping at the foot of that town's historic Broadway Street, where country music stars and tourists mingle among century old brick buildings that once catered to steamboat traffic.

To say that the river has witnessed history at that spot would be an understatement.

From the moccasin clad footsteps of the Native Americans to the patent leather boots of the flashy costumed singers on the stage of the old Ryman Auditorium, the birthplace of country music, history has been made there.

If ghosts walk the streets of the 'lower Broad' neighborhood, as locals refer to it, one place they would be seen is the corner of Fourth Avenue and Church Street, just two blocks away from where neon lights entice visitors today.

That is where the old Maxwell House Hotel stood from 1859, when its construction began...as talk of a civil war was just a much repeated whisper...to its loss by fire in 1961.

The Maxwell House had its share of triumph and tragedy.

The five story brick hotel was destined to be Nashville's premier hostelry. It would hold 240 rooms with facilities to host as many as 800 people for meetings, conventions and social galas.

At its grand opening in 1869, it advertised steam heat, gas lights and "a bathroom on each floor".

Rooms were four dollars a day, meals included.

And then, there was the coffee!

Maxwell House Coffee is still made and sold today, but was first served at this well known address.

Even though it would later entertain seven U.S. Presidents and such celebrities as Enrico Caruso, Annie Oakley, Thomas Edison and the author O'Henry, it was what happened before it opened that leads us to see ghosts and to hear the cries of men in agony and women weeping.

As we stated, construction was begun in 1859, just before the 1860 election of Abraham Lincoln, an election that plunged the nation into a blood bath...the deadliest war in American history.

John Overton, Jr. was the wealthy man behind the project, coming from a family associated with wealth and culture. His father was a lawyer, judge, plantation owner and friends with Andrew Jackson.

John Overton, Sr. and Jackson had founded the City of Memphis, Tennessee.

Overton Junior named the new hotel after his second wife, Harriet Maxwell.

The start of the war did not stop construction. Too much money had already been spent and money needed to be made if it was to be a success.

Besides, early in the war, confidence was strong that the conflict of brother against brother would be short and a new nation, the Confederate Staes of America, would survive and Nashville would be a major city in the new republic.

That hope was dashed in 1862 when Union troops occupied Nashville after the strategic loss of Ft. Donelson, further up the Cumberland River, which let the blue coats march unimpeded into the state's capital.

With occupation, the large hotel came under Union jurisdiction, and that led to its unfinished rooms being used as barracks for Yankee soldiers and as a temporary prison for captured Rebels.

More than one thousand soldiers were being held at the hotel in September of 1863, many of them in the upper floors. Four hundred men were packed on the top floor alone.

Although, much had been done to the exterior of the building, the staircase to the upper floors was unfinished, called 'temporary' in some accounts.

That is important to the story, because one day as the men from the fifth floor were using the staircase to go down to the main floor for breakfast, the stairs collapsed

It is suspected that a Union guard, for some reason or another, stopped the first few to arrive at the bottom of the staircase, which caused the men to bunch up on the stairs as they continued to enter from above.

Overloaded, or maybe due to a weak beam, the uppermost staircase gave a loud crack and collapsed.

As that set of stairs, men and all, fell to the fourth level, that level couldn't bear the additional weight and it too collapsed.

In all, four sets of stairs fell into a mess of splintered wood, broken bodies, dust and confusion...oh yes, the screams of men in panic, men in agony and men dying were in the mix.

Adding to the noise were the shouts of men in uniform, both blue and grey, rushing to help the injured, pulling bodies from the debris and then calling on horse drawn ambulances to take the bloodied men to hospitals.

Women of the city, all Confederate sympathizers, heard of the disaster and rushed to the site to help administer first aid...some of them already experienced from tending to battle wounded sons, brothers and fathers.

There, to add to the confusion, Union guards kept them back at bayonet point.

Now, their wails of distress added to the din.

Years later, one of the soldiers who was on the stairway when it collapsed, wrote his recollections stating, "There were 126 of us in the fall –45 killed outright or died in a short time...it was 22 days before I could stand up."

Efforts were made to keep news of the stair collapse quiet as battle dead were instead making headlines both north and south.

It was soon forgotten.

By 1961, when the old hotel burned, it had seen better days and that section of town, close by the river, was surrounded by bars and honkytonks with music blaring from their open doors.

Since then, that part of Nashville, now dubbed “Music City”, has quite changed. The once tawdry streets and souvenir shops are now prime real estate.

It is, as they say, “a happening place”!

Still, while there are probably ghosts enough to share with other sites and streets in town, we know that the ghosts at the corner of fourth Avenue and Church Street are the ghosts of the poor men who fell to their deaths in the stairway collapse of the old Maxwell House Hotel.

The Foggy Night

Nashville has been around a long time.

From Native Americans to French fur traders to the men and women who today sing on the stage of the Grand Ole Opry, its location on a bluff overlooking the Cumberland River has always been a draw.

At one time it was called Ft. Nashborough, named for revolutionary War general, Francis Nash, and using the old English "borough' to signify a town. By 1784, poor relations with the British led its residents to change from that to 'Nashville', using instead the French word 'ville' for town.

Ghosts no doubt roam its streets.

The ghost of this story only appears on foggy nights, which aren't too rare for a city close to a big river like the Cumberland.

I had the opportunity to interview an older gentleman, now retired after a life of teaching, and in our discussion, he mentioned his childhood home in Nashville...and, its spooky history.

As the house is still standing, although no longer in the man's family I won't divulge its location, but there is a lot I can tell.

Like many of the historic homes of Middle Tennessee, it started as a simple two story log home.

The logs were cut off the land around the estate.

The oldest log homes of both Tennessee and Kentucky were built of red cedar logs. If ever there was a tough old wood, that would be it! You can cut a fence post of red cedar and plant it in the ground and expect it to still be there one hundred years from now.

After all the large red cedar trees were cut, to build their log cabins the pioneers used oak, chestnut, yellow poplar and even cherry and walnut, as these trees grew wild and plentiful on the frontier.

As the family's fortunes improved, a large two story Georgian mansion was built and, because they so enjoyed the comfort of the old log cabin, the new house was connected to the old one.

Years later, brick wings were added to each side of the Georgian mansion.

Again, this is typical of many such old properties. An historian could stand on the front lawn of one of these impressive old homes and tell you the age just by looking at its original facade and additions.

Through the years, the house was able to weather the storms of mother nature, the intrusions of the Civil War and the economic turmoil of the Great Depression.

Eventually, the descendants of its early occupants wanted something more modern and the house was sold and occupied by a new family...a family that would soon find that strange things happened on foggy nights.

It was the family of the man telling me this story.

As he explained it, on a foggy night soon after he and his parents had moved in, the air being cool and moist, the family dogs suddenly began to bark.

The dogs ran to the front door as if there was someone outside.

Yet, no one knocked on the door and when the father opened the door, there was no one standing on the porch.

The fog had settled on the expansive lawn, so that a person couldn't see far and perhaps someone was out there and had been scared off by the barking of the dogs.

But, no one responded to a call of "Who's there?"

Closing the door, the father noticed that the dogs had changed their demeanor, backing up from the hallway as if someone was standing there.

Calling the family to witness, the father pointed out the dog's strange behavior...they seemed to be looking at someone nobody else in the house could see.

The dogs' stares then followed this invisible entity down the hall to a door on the underside of the stairs...a door that led to another set of stairs, stairs leading down to a rock walled cellar.

After a moment of staring at the cellar door, the dogs seemed agitated again and whined and barked for a few minutes, looking nervously from the cellar door to the members of the family standing there.

This led the father to open the door to the cellar.

If he expected to see someone, he was disappointed.

There was no one there.

When invited to investigate, the dogs ignored the father's suggestion and after a few moments, wined until the father shut the door.

That was it.

The dogs regained their composure and returned to their former occupation of lying on the floor of the living room, at the foot of the father's chair.

This antic by the dogs was repeated every time fog descended on the house after the sun had gone down.

And, just like before, there was never anyone at the door to the house or on the cellar stairs.

Confused by their four-legged companions, the father decided to do a little historic investigation.

Murder most foul had been committed on the property.

It was, the father found out, a local tale that a young lady had been murdered on the property.

The murder, as you might surmise, took place in the cellar of the large old home.

But, there was more!

The murder had taken place on a foggy night!

Was the ghost of the old house agitated by having new occupants or had the former residents neglected to tell them about their resident ghost.

As far as my friend knows, the strange visitor continues to enter the house on foggy nights.

I asked him a question.

"Who", I said, "is this ghost? Is it the ghost of the poor young lady, returning...or is it the ghost of the murderer, doomed for eternity to revisit the scene of his dastardly crime?"

"That's a good question," my friend told me.

"And, it is one I can't answer!"

Perhaps, you, the reader of this woeful tale, have an opinion!

WSM GRAND

Ghosts at the Ryman

There is probably no better known entertainment venue closer to the swirling waters of the Cumberland River than Nashville's Ryman Auditorium.

Often called "The Mother Church of Country Music", it is a building known worldwide as the home of the Grand Ole Opry, with a history inhabited by preachers, steamboat captains, politicians, soldiers, musicians and entertainers of every stripe, color and musical note.

Oh yes, it also has ghosts!

But, let's start at the beginning...

A man born in Alabama in 1847 had a fine education, became a lawyer and then got lost in his success, his wealth and the demon rum.

Sam Jones, however, turned his life around and swore off alcohol, studied ministry and became an ordained Methodist preacher. Not just an ordinary man of the cloth, Sam Jones was an evangelist...he preached to the lost and brought them to the faith.

He spoke with the strength of conviction that only comes from someone who has been there.

In no time at all, he was the most prominent revivalist in the South, the Bible Belt of the nation.

Condemning mankind's lust for money, he once said, "...ye men could be toiled to hell by having a nickel every ten feet along the path." He didn't hesitate to "tell it like it is"!

At a revival in San Antonio, Texas, he compared the city to the devil's den, saying that the only difference between the two was that one of them had a river running down the middle of it.

In 1885, Sam Jones led a big tent revival in Nashville.

It was a big tent and a big crowd. Nashville didn't have a church large enough to hold the mass of people who came to hear Sam Jones speak.

One of the men in the crowd was riverboat captain Thomas Ryman.

Ryman had worked his way up from the bottom. He has sold fish, hauled freight and studied the waters of the Tennessee and Cumberland rivers. In time, he began his own steamboat line, carrying tobacco, cotton, corn, lumber, livestock and passengers up and down the rivers.

Ryman worked the Cumberland River likes Jones worked the Bible, hard and earnest.

One big difference was that much of Ryman's prosperity lay in selling whiskey to passengers on his steamboats and allowing a little gambling. He didn't miss the opportunity to make a dollar.

Sam Jones preached against alcohol and those who profited from it

Thomas Ryman attended the Nashville revival not to hear a lecture on sobriety, but to heckle Sam Jones, the speaker. Taking a few roustabouts with him, he intended to disrupt the proceedings.

It didn't go as planned!

Tom Ryman fell to his knees and was converted by the robust eloquence of Sam Jones. He vowed to never take another drink and to halt all liquor sales on his boats.

Professing his new-found faith to Jones, Ryman wanted to do something for the people of Nashville who, like him, needed to hear the word of the Lord.

Right then and there, Ryman made plans to build a brick edifice big enough to hold the crowds that Sam Jones attracted and he did just that.

Pledging money of his own and persuading others to pitch in, land was purchased just a short distance from the Cumberland River and the foundation dug.

A year later, Sam Jones preached a revival standing in the unfinished building surrounded by walls only six feet high.

It was to be called the "Union Gospel Tabernacle", 'union' to imply that it was not for only one Christian denomination, but for all to share.

Seven years after the first shovel of dirt was turned over, the building was finished. It had cost one hundred thousand dollars and was twenty thousand dollars in debt. Plans originally included a balcony, but there wasn't enough money to build it.

During the construction, Sam Jones had suggested the tabernacle be named after Tom Ryman, but he had refused the honor.

Later, the building did get its balcony.

To be large enough to host an 1897 meeting of the United Confederate Veterans, money from that group added the balcony, emblazoning it with the words, "Confederate Gallery".

When Thomas Ryman died in 1904, Sam Jones preached his funeral. Afterwards, he again recommended naming the building for his friend and fellow believer. In that year it became the 'Ryman Auditorium'.

Two years later, Jones was also dead.

The auditorium was Nashville's largest entertainment house. A stage had been added in 1901 and the building was being used for more than revivals.

In 1913, blind celebrity Helen Keller gave a lecture to a sold-out crowd.

Other big names to walk across the stage included Henry Houdini, W.C. Fields, Will Rogers, Charlie Chaplin and Teddy Roosevelt.

Three Tennessee governors held their inaugurations there.

And there was music other than gospel, opera singer Enrico Caruso, the Fisk Jubilee Singers, orchestras, solo instrumentalists and music revues.

Which leads us to our first ghost.

Sam Jones had preached against liquor, dancing, idleness and the theatre. But, to keep up with the big building's maintenance, the Ryman was now playing host to stage productions...theatre.

And that is when people began to hear the ghost of Sam Jones pounding on the floor backstage, just as he had pounded his feet on the floors of churches as he preached and pounded his Bible on their pulpits.

The people in their seats heard the pounding too.

Members of the audience for a performance of the opera "Carmen" were able to hear a pounding noise over the sounds of the singers and the orchestra.

But, there are more ghosts than Sam Jones.

In the 1920's radio was a novelty, but also very popular. It brought news to homes across the nation...and music.

Radio station WSM in Nashville began to host a weekly music show and found that listeners liked to hear the old tunes played on banjo and fiddle and 'the Grand Ole Opry' was born.

At that time the station allowed the public to attend the live shows and to clap and applaud the performers.

But, their station was limited in size. The crowds wanting to see the show were large, and in 1942, the show was moved to the Ryman Auditorium.

For the next thirty-one years, until it moved to a new location elsewhere in Nashville, it was the home to a music show that captured the ears and hearts of rural families in the deep South and out West and as far north as Canada.

Which brings us to a couple more ghosts.

The singers and musicians of the Opry have known poverty, have played beer joints and honky-tonks for pennies, had dreams broken and fulfilled, hearts busted and loves lost, addictions and sorrow...it's what they sing about.

Two of those stars of the Grand Old Opry are said to linger on the stage, both having died young and tragically.

Patsy Cline was at the top of her career when she was killed in a small plane crash, leaving behind a husband and two children.

Her road to the top from poverty has been told in movies and stage productions. Even today, if you find a jukebox, you will find "Crazy" and "Walking After Midnight" as selections.

Workers at the Ryman, as they close up at night after the crowds are gone... for the Ryman still plays host to musicians... say they can hear her singing off in the distance. Guides to the building have heard her as has the occasional visitor.

On that old oak stage, Patsy Cline can sing as if she were still alive and life was good and the people behind the footlights loved her.

She is not alone on the stage.

Like Patsy, Hank Williams, Sr. rose from having little to the top of his profession. He had tough times and good. He had love and lost it. He had addictions and they took their toll on him.

Williams died at age twenty-nine, a victim of alcohol and drug abuse, leaving us such classic country music songs as "Your Cheating Heart", "I'm So Lonesome I Can Cry" and "I Saw the

Light".

Hank too, is heard at night by people cleaning up, or those who arrive early and open up the building for tours. Other entertainers claim to have heard his distinctive voice off in the distance, as plaintive as ever.

And, there is one more ghost.

Remember the story of the balcony and how it got built.

People setting up for shows will tell you they have seen a man, sitting alone in the balcony, dressed in grey like a Confederate soldier. He sits and watches, never speaking or causing a problem. If someone goes to investigate, he disappears.

Just one more ghost to live in the old Ryman!

Does A Governor Haunt a Hotel?

Every small town had a hotel, back in the old days.

Towns, you may have noticed, seem to be arranged on the map equidistance from each other...about fifteen miles apart.

The reason is simple enough. In the days of the pioneers, walking from one town to the next or even riding a horse over dirt roads with creeks to ford, the best you could travel in one day was about fifteen miles...give or take a few miles if the trail was on flat land or hilly!

So, towns sprang up a day's travel apart.

In this ghost story, we visit an old hotel in a small town, a town with a railroad.

Now, railroads also come with ghost stories!

Many states have tales of headless brakemen who worked for the railroad, forever looking for their heads. Which, according to legends, were cut off in a tragic rail accident. The poor brakemen are forever doomed to walk the tracks at night, swinging their lanterns, looking for their heads.

How a headless man can expect to find anything is beyond me, but I am just repeating the stories.

In Dickson, Tennessee, in the county of the same name, it is the Hotel Halbrook that is haunted.

The county seat, Dickson is not a large town, but its closeness to Nashville has made it a popular place to live for those who don't mind a commute.

In 1913, when the hotel was built, people didn't have the luxury of hopping into their cars and driving an hour down a paved highway, which is why the town needed a hotel. Traveling salesmen in the early 1900's could crisscross the state in horse drawn wagons, or take the train to those towns on the railroad, like Dickson.

Once in the hotel, a salesman could call on town businesses and then rent a horse and buggy from a livery stable to call on the small country stores across the county.

A hotel allowed a salesman to have a place to stay every night of his visit as opposed to having to knock on a farmhouse door and ask if the farm family could put him up for the night...hopefully in a spare bedroom and not in the barn!

Women didn't have much choice in jobs in 1913, when the Hotel Halbrook was built, as they were expected to get married and raise a family, not take a job as a salesperson!

But, some women would get an education and become school teachers...or, they could run a boarding house or a hotel.

Which brings us to a ghost that occupies the Hotel Halbrook.

The lady in question may have been the manager and she had a problem with people who dragged their feet as they trod up the hotel stairs.

Today, if you are walking heavily up the stairs, creating a little racket...if you are lucky... you may hear a woman's voice shout out, "Pick up your feet!"

Similar unexplained voices and noises at the old hotel can make workers there uneasy, but it has also led to having 'paranormal research' done by people with gizmos that detect the presence of ...ghosts!

No longer a working hotel, the large brick structure now bills itself as the "Clement Railroad Hotel Museum".

The name 'Clement' has significance. You see, one of the former residents of Dickson was Frank Clement. Clement was a popular Tennessee governor in the 1950's and 60's and is recognized with displays in the museum.

Clement is another ghost who is said to sometimes walk the hallways or drift up the century old stairs...being careful not to make too much noise, we suspect. He has more than a passing attachment to the old hotel...he was born there! His mother ran the hotel at one time.

She may be the source of the voice admonishing us to tip toe lightly up the stairs!

Meanwhile, a person with one of those paranormal machines has investigated the premises, and reports that the air of the hotel is rich with 'activity'.

As far as we are concerned, if all the ghost expects us to do is 'pick up our feet', then we shouldn't find it too scary to visit Dickson and the museum...and, museums are always full of interesting old things besides the occasional ghost.

The Bell Witch

The Bell family were wealthy residents in the town of Adams, Tennessee. They are also part of the state's best known ghost story.

Adams, never a big town, lies on the Red River, one of the largest tributaries of the Cumberland River. People were living in the area by 1791.

John Bell, a farmer, moved his family from North Carolina to Adams in 1805.

There was no hint of a ghost or unusual happenings until in 1816, strange things began to take place, such as weird animals seen on the property, the sound of someone knocking on the walls, voices in the dark and other unexplained sounds.

A dead woman, named 'Kate', the family decided, was the source of all this disharmony. She was, they concluded, a witch.

The stories associated with the Bell Witch are too many to tell here, except that after John Bell's death, she seems to have retired to a nearby cave and stopped her tricks.

Which leads us to a more recent visit by Kate and one that, while not as woeful as that of John Bell, is none-the-less spooky.

I had the opportunity to interview one of the victims, who as can be imagined, does not want his real name used.

But, here is Bob's tale, in his own words:

"I was a student at a college in Nashville in the late 1960's.

As students, on weekends we would stay up late watching the only TV in the building, in the dorm lobby, talking and joking around.

One of our group was from a small town close to Adams and told us the story of Kate, the Bell Witch. I was from out of state, as were most of us.

His name was 'Andy'.

Well, Andy said that the Bell Witch lived in a cave and he had been to it many times. He said it was close to the road and easy to get to.

One thing led to another and we organized a trip to see the Bell Witch, for the next afternoon, which was Saturday.

By the time we left on the next day, we had two car loads of skeptical young men. Few of us had cars back then, so we had to all pile into those two cars.

I rode with 'Jimmy', a Yankee who was particularly amused by the legend. I was from out West, but less vocal about my disbelief. I do remember that Andy told us that the Bell Witch didn't like to be bothered. I think he was laughing when he told us that bit of information.

Andy and another fellow were on the front with Jimmy and I was sitting on the back seat. There were four of us on that seat, seven altogether. We led the expedition because Andy knew the way. An upper classman named 'Dewayne' had the second car. It too was full.

The drive took us longer than we had planned. I think we stopped on the way and got cold drinks and snacks. We were in no particular hurry.

It was getting dark by the time we got to Adams and Andy immediately took us down several wrong roads before he got his bearings. Then, he decided to show us the Bell family cemetery first.

By now it was dark.

We got out at the small cemetery. It was out in the country and there were no homes nearby. I remember it being very quiet.

We were a little intimidated by the thought of walking in a cemetery at night in a strange town with no real reason to be there, except curiosity.

Yet, what happened next was only a hint of what was to follow.

Andy pointed to a tombstone and said something to the effect that he thought that was the grave of John Bell. One of us said, "I'll go see", and stepped through an iron gate and into the cemetery.

As soon as he did, a dog began to howl in the distance, followed by the other dogs down the road, as if on cue! I think we woke up every dog in the county!

Not knowing who might investigate this sudden chorus of howling, we immediately left and continued to wander up the road till Andy finally saw a wood sign. It said, 'Bell Witch Cave' and had an arrow pointing in the direction down the road. The sign looked old, as if the cave had once been a tourist attraction.

Jimmy drove in the direction the faded arrow pointed us.

We turned where Andy told us, onto an old dirt road, down a short hill to an old barn.

One more thing.

As we drove down the hill to the barn, we drove past an ancient house that appeared to be unoccupied. At least, there were no lights on and we didn't see a car or truck parked close by.

We piled out of the two cars. Boy, were we excited. Andy had told us that the cave didn't have lights, so I stayed close to my roommate 'Tim', who had a flashlight.

I think there was another old sign by the barn with an arrow. My memory is a little fuzzy after all these years, but I clearly remember what happened next.

We suddenly heard a loud voice, a woman's voice, a very agitated woman, "Who's down there?"

We all turned to face the old house and could just make out a woman's head sticking out of an upstairs' window, a faint light behind her.

She hollered again, "Who's down there?"

I turned to look at Andy, thinking, "What's this all about?", but before he could do some explaining the lady yelled again. Her voice was a little more agitated. "My husband's got his gun and he's coming down there!" There was no discussion on our part.

We all rushed back to the cars!

I can still see Dewayne's group pile into his car, barely pulling their doors shut before he peeled out, throwing dirt and gravel in our direction.

The rest of us were gathered around Jimmy's car waiting because, for no logical reason, he had locked his car.

As he fumbled through his pockets, I was anxiously keeping my eyes on the front door of the house, hoping we could follow Dewayne before the woman's husband and his gun stepped out onto the porch.

In hindsight I realize the Bell Witch was playing games with us, because Jimmy looked at me and whispered, "I can't find my keys!"

Tim was beside me and heard what Jimmy said.

He yelled, "WHAT?"

Now, was not the time to panic!

Tim flashed his light into the car.

There, plain to see, were Jimmy's keys, still in the car ignition.

For the first time in his life, Jimmy had locked his keys inside his car!

I heard the screen door on the porch slam shut.

I looked towards the house.

I swear I saw the moonlight gleam on the barrel of the gun the man was holding in his hand as he stepped off the porch and started towards us.

Now, was the time to panic!

I remember six boys running in every direction. I specifically recall seeing one of us dive headfirst over a barbed wire fence.

But, I stood my ground.

To my way of thinking, I hadn't done anything wrong except a minor case of trespassing based on the false narrative of Andy.

I raised both my hands over my head as if to surrender, just like I had seen people do in the movies. And, I walked slowly up the hill to meet the man with the big gun.

I don't remember just what I said, but I am sure I mumbled some apology and tried to explain the situation while the man with the big gun stood there and listened quietly.

I think he shook his head in disbelief.

But, he turned his head and yelled back up to the house to tell his wife not to call the police...and, he put the gun down.

I still had my hands in the air. Now though, I put them down and the man walked with me over to the car to see for himself.

I called to the other guys to come out and the man directed us all to look around the ground for a piece of wire, for he was sure there would be some around the barn or fence row.

With his help, and a piece of fence wire, we managed to get Jimmy's car unlocked.

We all profusely apologized and swore to never bother he or his wife again or to come looking for the Bell Witch.

I think he may have even laughed at us.

Back in the car, Jimmy drove up the short hill and out of Adams, glad that our rear ends hadn't been the target of the man's big gun.

As we drove off, we did look anxiously around for Dewayne, thinking he and his crew would have stopped a short distance down the road waiting for us, but there was no sign of them.

We were tired and sleepy all the way back to Nashville and the campus and the dorm, where in the lobby we found Dewayne and the others.

At least they had waited to see if we were still alive.

We recounted our adventures with the group conclusion that the Bell Witch had put her 'whammy' on us. That was as close to being shot as I have ever been in my life, even to this day, fifty or more years later.

Dewayne looked sheepish as we had told our story, I supposed from his embarrassment in going off and leaving us.

But, that wasn't the case.

One of his crew said something like, "Tell 'em, Dewayne. Tell 'em what happened!"

He looked at us and half laughing, confessed "We got a speeding ticket on our way back to town!"

"Well, if that's not proof that the Bell Witch is still out there causing trouble, I don't' know what is!"

I agree!

Clarksville's Lonely Widow

As we alluded to earlier, ghosts seem to appear when they have suffered a great loss and haunt a house or building as if they won't let death take them away from that place of grief.

Such is the case of Lucy Smith, Clarksville, Tennessee's, resident ghost, who to this day mourns the death of her husband, Christopher.

As young lovers, Christopher and Lucy were blessed with all the comforts that wealth could offer in the pre-Civil War South.

Having made his fortune in tobacco, in 1858 Smith built a magnificent home for his wife.

"Nothing but the best" as they say!

Located on a rise overlooking the Cumberland River, the two-story Italianate home was built of brick, at a time when brick was made by hand, usually with slave labor, made from clay dug close by and fired on the property.

The arched windows were a sign to the bustling river town that the Smith family were up to date with the latest designs and trends in construction.

The house is said to have been drawn up by Adolphus Heiman of Nashville, who had designed some of that city's largest churches as well as 'Belmont', the home of wealthy Adelicia Acklen and today the centerpiece of Belmont University.

Furnishings would have come from New Orleans or Philadelphia. One of the notable aspects of the house was a small balcony on the front.

It was placed there, it is said, so that Lucy Smith could look down at the river to see her husband arrive by steamboat, for he was also a steamboat captain.

The house also has a 'widow's walk'.

Homes on the East Coast of this country have small balconies placed on the roofs of large ocean front homes, where sea captain wives could look out and see their husbands' ships arrive after months at sea.

We call those small balconies 'widows' walks' because too often the women who stood and looked out over the blue sea would be given the sad news that their husbands' ships had gone down in a gale, leaving them widows.

While the Smith home has a widow's walk, it is the balcony that has a ghostly visitor.

You see, Lucy stood on her balcony waiting for a husband who never returned.

In 1865, Christopher Smith took ill in New Orleans with yellow fever, a disease so terrible and deadly that people would flee to the countryside whenever it took a sojourn in their city, convinced it was 'bad air' that had enveloped the town, unaware that the disease was spread by the lowly mosquito.

Yet, Christopher's death was only part of Lucy's suffering.

The steamboat bringing her husband's body back to Clarksville sank in an accident and many people perished when the boat went down.

Christopher's body was never recovered.

Since her death, residents of Clarksville report seeing her ghost on the balcony of her home, walking and waiting.

Does Lucy pace back and forth expecting a man who will never arrive or is she fully aware that no amount of walking to and fro will ever bring her loved one back, but stands there looking out on the river trying to recall happier times?

Whatever the case, people still claim to see her ghostly form roaming about the old home, for it is still standing. It is now owned by the city and is still impressive after all these years.

If you pass through Clarksville, wait till night falls and if it is a moonless night, cast your eyes on the façade of the Smith house and maybe you too will see Lucy's ghostly form standing on the little balcony, perhaps waiting for her husband's ghost to join her in death.

Don't Disturb a Cemetery!

Tennessee and Kentucky, like other states in the South, have a large number of cemeteries.

In my job as a county historian, I keep track of almost three hundred cemeteries, and ours is a small county. That's because, in the past, when a family member died, they were buried close to their home. Consequently, every family had its own small graveyard.

That was the method used for at least the first hundred years of settlement, until towns grew large enough to establish a common 'burying ground' for the public.

Before emancipation, slaves were buried to the side of the white family cemetery, usually with just a rock to mark the grave. Even white family cemeteries would often use large rocks to mark a grave. Hand cut and engraved tombstones were difficult to procure and expensive to boot.

Let's note here that the history of tombstones is in itself kinda spooky!

In the ancient past, perhaps due to a belief in ghosts or perhaps due to old superstitions, people were afraid that dead people's spirits might leave their graves and come around at night to haunt or bother the living.

The first tombstones were simply very large rocks placed on graves to keep those dead spirits in place!

With time, to keep the family from getting confused as to who was buried where, names were scratched on the big rocks...and, tombstones were born!

I told you it was kinda spooky.

I would like to say that, "Well, people today don't believe such hogwash!", but then why am I writing a book on ghosts and why are you reading it?

While some family cemeteries are large, with fences or rocks walls around them, most family cemeteries are small. As families died out or moved on, the small ones tended to be forgotten and, much too often, neglected. Weeds began to grow, then shrubs and then trees took root, until the stones were all but gone from view.

In our present day and times, laws have been put on the books to protect family cemeteries. Legally, a landowner can't destroy or move old tombstones. Real estate agents must notify a person buying a lot that a cemetery is on the property. Also, descendants can't be denied access to the cemetery if they want to visit or want to maintain the grave site.

Some families sponsor an annual day for cleaning up their ancestor's final resting places...many don't.

That was sadly the case of the old Pegram family cemetery in Cheatham County, Tennessee. Not only was the cemetery overgrown and neglected, it was bulldozed over by real estate developers.

This happened in the early 1970's before the state passed legislation to protect cemeteries.

It's not that the developers were not aware of the cemetery, it's just that legally at that time, they could do as they pleased with the graves...and they did just that.

A small subdivision, Harpeth Haven, was built on a piece of property that included the old Pegram family cemetery.

Named for the Harpeth River, that runs into the Cumberland River nearby, the subdivision had a pleasant location and residents were content...until 1975 when a heavy rain caused the Harpeth River to overflow its banks.

That's when the water soaked land caused some long buried coffins to float to the surface!

One of those was the coffin of a member of the Pegram family, the same family that lent its name to the nearby town of Pegram.

That was a problem.

It's not clear whose responsibility it is to rebury a coffin when it suddenly emerges from your back yard!

But, the question was soon in the news and the incident was covered by the local radio station and newspaper...even the Nashville television stations took an interest.

The location of the subdivision was news.

Was it a bad decision to place new homes so close to the river and was it an equally bad decision to build them over a cemetery?

Local residents began to wonder if the location was cursed...if the subdivision and even the little town of Pegram were cursed for not respecting the dead!

It was pointed out that the town had been having a run of bad luck lately. With only three thousand residents, Pegram had been having some issues!

A newly built civic building seemed to have an unusual run of problems, causing construction overruns of hundreds of thousands of dollars.

The town's new sewer system had complications.

Even the volunteer fire department complained of fires that were out, but seemed to re-ignite?

Yep, it was all because the real estate developer had bulldozed the cemetery and had even sold some of the dirt. The dirt was used here and there around Pegram...maybe, the dirt carried the curse with it.

Throw in some unusual noises in the night winds, strange shadows appearing here and there and some people were convinced that the whole area was haunted.

Or, it could simply be people's imaginations running away with them.

One thing is for certain...don't disturb the graves of anyone from Native Americans to the pioneers to military graveyards to the present...let the dead rest in peace!

Don't say you haven't been warned!

Ghosts in Blue and Gray

That there are ghosts who haunt the Civil War battlefields of Tennessee should come as no surprise.

Tennessee is second only to Virginia in the number of battles fought on its soil. Hence, it is called "the battleground of the Confederacy."

Shiloh, Chickamauga, the Battle of the Clouds, Fort Donelson, the battles of Murfreesboro, Franklin, Nashville, Stones River, Missionary Ridge and Chattanooga are just some of the many sieges to take place in the 'Volunteer State.'

For a short time, the Cumberland River was the border between North and South and iron clad gunboats once made their way up the river past Nashville and as far as Carthage.

The state was unique in other ways.

Tennessee was the last state to succeed from the Union and the first to return!

Roughly 100,000 of Tennessee's sons fought for the rebellion. Another 50,000 fought to save the Union.

The state's African American population was also involved, with the first troop of freemen and recently freed slaves mustered in Gallatin, a town on the Cumberland River. Black men of Tennessee would go on to fill eight artillery units, twenty-two infantry units and one cavalry unit.

With so many battles fought in the state, plus countless skirmishes, (the difference being that skirmishes involve fewer men and are for a shorter engagement), there are many graveyards as well.

The American Civil War averaged, in its four years, 599 deaths a day, making it the deadliest war Americans have fought.

Another statistic is that 90 percent of the deaths during that bloody division between Rebel and Yankee, were not in combat but were from infections the men developed as a result of their wounds.

Every battlefield, whether set aside as a memorial park or simply a patch of land beside a highway with a small plaque marking the spot, has its own 'ghost' stories.

We will look at one battle, and its ghosts, that took place right on the river.

In the early months of the war, the dividing border between the United Staes of America and the Confederates States of America, was expected to be the Ohio River. That thinking was lost when Kentucky stayed with the Union, throwing the border into Tennessee.

As Union troops entered Kentucky, a defensible line between the two nations was difficult to create, but one was quickly drawn up when the South hastily built two forts, Fort Henry on the Tennessee River and Fort Donelson on the Cumberland. Both rivers empty into the Ohio in western Kentucky.

The Battles for the two, in February of 1862, would decide where the two nations met and would also be pivotal in the career of General Ulysses S. Grant.

A quick summary:

Fort Henry, only twelve miles from Fort Donelson, was the first to fall into Union hands. Built right on the banks of the Tennessee River, it was poorly designed and when rains caused the river to flood, water damaged the fort and water got into the fort's powder magazine. Heavy fire from Union gun boats further tipped the battle to the Yankee's favor.

On February 6th, when the Confederate command of the fort surrendered, it was before General Grant and his army had even arrived!

Grant didn't tarry at the site of the defeated Rebels and immediately led his army the short distance to Fort Donelson, overlooking the Cumberland River.

Better built and designed, the fort on the Cumberland had big cannons aimed at anyone or anything that might attempt to pass up the river.

By February 11th, Grant's army was in place and ready for the battle to begin.

Poor leadership by the Southern command, cold weather, an intense assault by the Union Army, and the firepower of the Union gunboats led to the surrender of the fort...after only five days of fighting.

But, there was more!

When Confederate General Buckner asked for the terms of surrender, General Grant responded, "No terms except unconditional and immediate surrender can be accepted."

That infamous demand led to Grant's subsequent nickname of 'Unconditional Surrender Grant'.

In the aftermath of the battle, Tennessee's state capital of Nashville was abandoned by the Confederate Army and the Cumberland River became the border between North and South as Union troops occupied the city.

Visitors to the battlefield today are impressed by its well-kept park like setting, its visitor's center and its magnificent views of the Cumberland River.

Few people stay after dark to wait for any spirits or ghosts to appear, but some have!

When, several years ago, a group of Civil War re-enactors pitched tents on the battlefield...with the permission of park officials...they reported noises and sounds they couldn't explain, sounds like that of a battle being fought close by.

But, one soldier in particular later confessed to seeing something he also couldn't explain.

As he stood on the battlefield, after dark, in his re-enactor's uniform, he saw a light approaching. The light, he would go on to explain, seemed to come from a lit cigar held tight in the mouth of a man in a blue uniform, a man wearing a wide brim hat.

When the man got closer, the re-enactor realized he wasn't looking at simply another reenactor but a man that looked strangely like Union General Ulysses S. Grant.

It was then that the re-enactor noticed that the lower portion of the man's body was missing and that the man seemed to be floating in the dark night air.

As he watched, the ghostly apparition proceeded on its way, as if going over the battlefield encampment to check on his soldiers, just as a general might do before lying down for the night himself.

Grant's ghost, if indeed that is what the reenactor saw, was far from his actual resting place, for "Grant's Tomb' is in New York City, New York!

A Haunted Bridge

Now, you may ask yourself, "How can a bridge be haunted?" And, that would be a good question to ponder!

The bridge in this story, however, doesn't have just one ghost, but three spectral visitors.

Located in Trigg County, Kentucky, the small bridge enjoys the visits of the local teenagers on dark nights, all anxious to see the ghosts in person. We won't give directions, since the neighbors don't always appreciate traffic up and down their otherwise quiet back country road.

To return to our first question, 'how can a bridge be haunted'?

Well, the bridge is pretty harmless. But, like some of the haunted houses we have visited, several ghosts have seemingly taken up residence there.

The first is the spirit of a woman who died near by and is said to walk the bridge, late at night, especially on foggy nights.

But, our lady is not alone.

A young couple who died in a car accident close to the bridge have also taken up residence.

Maybe, looking at what eternity offered them, at death's door they decided to stay here on earth, together...lest they be separated on the other side.

I have personally heard of this ghost from a friend who grew up in the neighborhood. He said, the challenge to he and his friends, while growing up, was to drive onto the bridge late at night and stop in the middle. Then, they were to turn off the engine and wait for one of the ghosts to appear.

Scary enough, you say!

The challenge failed to mention that when you saw something unexplained hovering in the night air, or a disembodied face looking in your rearview window, that when you tried to start your car, the engine would be 'dead'.

How appropriate!

If you heard footsteps approaching, the closer they got, the harder it was to get the engine to turn over, till, finally, just as the footsteps or apparition got close enough to reach out and touch you...the car would start and you would drive off in a frenzy!

Others, skeptical of the power of a ghost to control car batteries or sparkplugs, have stopped on the bridge and had no problem...even though they too have seen something they couldn't quite explain, something that looked like a ghost of a woman.

So, we leave it up to you to decide.

Would you take the risk of having to abandon your vehicle on a lonely country bridge and have to run back into town using your own two feet? Or, can you just smile when someone says a bridge is haunted and think to yourself, "Maybe, but I'll just take your word for it and keep myself at home on dark foggy nights!"

Castle on the Cumberland

Eddyville, Kentucky, has a castle!

This impressive building is made of massive granite blocks quarried close by, cut and set in place by Italian stone masons brought to this country for its construction.

It took four years to erect from start to finish.

The cost of building a castle is, as can be imagined, astronomical.

The larger the castle, the larger the sum of money spent to build it.

And, this is no ordinary castle.

It was built to house over 800 people...for you see, this huge stone edifice is the Kentucky State Prison, built between 1886 and 1890.

We might point out that when it was the decision of the Commonwealth of Kentucky...they prefer to not be called a 'state'...to build a new prison, it was thought that the more 'massive and thick' a prison's walls were, the better it would keep convicted felons in place.

The Kentucky State Prison looks like a medieval castle with it thick walls and huge towers. The prison so resembles a castle that it has been given the moniker, 'Castle on the Cumberland.'

Built on a hill, it does indeed overlook the Cumberland River at Eddyville, not far from where the river empties into the Ohio River.

When Lake Barkley was created by the construction of Barkley Dam in 1966, parts of the old town of Eddyville were covered by waters backed up by the dam.

To add to the drama of the prison's location, it is said that on occasion lights can be seen moving about in the old part of town now covered by Lake Barkley's waters...the lights are it is said, the souls of people who once lived there.

The prison, however, has enough unexplained happenings to keep a ghost hunter busy without having to look beneath the murky waters covering old Eddyville.

The oldest prison in Kentucky, it is used to house convicts who can't be held in the state's other jails or prisons due to their violent behavior. Or, as a resident of Eddyville has been heard to say, "the worse of the worse".

It was, in the past, where all of Kentucky's executions took place.

Though no longer in use, the prison held an electric chair, with the apt nickname "old Sparky".

That's a touch of gallows' humor.

But, there is nothing humorous about the chair.

It snuffed out the lives of 163 men between 1911, when it was installed, and 1962 when it was deemed too violent and lethal injections became a more acceptable form of execution.

Before the chair, men were hung by the neck until dead.

Old Sparky saw its busiest night in July of 1928, when seven men were electrocuted one by one in quick succession. Taken from their cells on 'death row', starting at fifteen minutes after midnight, the men were led to the chair.

By daybreak, seven white painted caskets were lined up by the prison guards for the families of the executed to pick up.

It is a sad note to make, but the prison has its own small cemetery for men who have died at the castle, in one manner or another, and had no one to ask for their remains.

If that's not a good source for ghosts, we would be surprised.

So, are there ghosts?

You bet!

Guards at the prison have reported strange sounds, loud knocks, screams in the night, ghostly shadows and moving apparitions.

One former guard has even written a book about the Castle on the Cumberland in which he related looking in a mirror and seeing the reflection of another man standing behind him...a man in the striped uniform of a prisoner.

When he turned around, there was no one there!

There are other stories, enough to fill a book!

We'll just say that the Castle on the Cumberland has its share of ghosts...the spirits of men ostracized by society, locked up, forgotten by family and left to waste away behind thick granite walls.

I think if I was one of those men buried in the prison cemetery or one of those who died having 700 volts of electricity course through their bodies, I would be tempted to be a ghost, and come back from the grave to spook a guard or a prison warden in my own little touch of "gallows humor!"

The River Ends with a Song

The Cumberland River ends in Smithland, Kentucky.

Between Smithland and the hills of Kentucky, it has traveled hundreds of miles, most of those miles in Tennessee.

All along its leisurely path, we have visited ghosts, strange lights, unexplained noises, disembodied voices and more.

We're not done yet!

Smithland too has a ghost story!

Despite being one of Kentucky's least populated counties and Smithland itself having less than five hundred inhabitants it claims an interesting spot in Kentucky history.

Its location, where the Cumberland enters the mighty Ohio River, led to its early occupation and settlement. Travelers would naturally stop there before entering that river... and, the Tennessee River enters the Ohio just twelve miles downstream.

About 1780, a large brick inn and tavern were built close to the river's edge.

That the old inn is still standing today is a testament to the skilled hands that built it, many of those workers being slaves.

It is a fine brick structure, two stories high, with its handmade bricks fired close by and then laid into walls sixteen inches thick.

Now known as the 'Gower House' after an early owner, it has fourteen rooms and almost as many fireplaces. A fire in 1857 destroyed a wing of the inn, which means that at one time it was much larger.

While its size and age are indeed impressive, it has a guest register that is even more astonishing.

Three presidents are known to have been overnight guests at the inn, Andrew Jackson, James K. Polk and Zachary Taylor. Taylor was informed he had won the presidency while staying at the inn!

Abraham Lincoln stopped there, as did Aaron Burr, Benedict Arnold and wildlife artist John James Audubon.

Those are just the tip of the iceberg!

Clara Barton, founder of the American Red Cross; Henry Clay, Kentucky politician and presidential candidate; General Lew Wallace, author of "Ben Hur"; Jenny Lind, the 'Swedish Nightingale"; Ned Buntline, father of the Dime Novel; General Lafayette, French soldier and hero of the American Revolution; and Charles Dickens, the celebrated English Author, all stayed at the inn.

Those are just the really famous.

Over the years the old inn has fed and housed countless travelers of every description and economic background.

And, as if that is not enough distinction, it may have played a part in the 'underground railroad', used by slaves to escape their bondage as they traveled north to freedom.

The building doubled as a courthouse in its early days, Smithland being the county seat of Livingston County, Kentucky. As such, court was held there and Henry Clay presided over at least one trial.

So, in addition to our list of celebrities, we can add a roster of less desirables...thieves, crooks and murderers.

Legend has it that a public hanging took place on the property.

Let's be clear about ghosts and their hauntings. Not all ghosts who linger about to spook the living, have met a grisly death there.

Some ghosts have died peacefully in their beds, having had ordinary lives.

What makes a dead person become a ghost can't be justified by an unfair or untimely death...although, that seems to be the case for most of the spirits we have met in this book...they may have died elsewhere but return to a place that was significant during their lifetimes, to them at least.

Which brings us to the Gower house and at least one ghost that people claim to have encountered.

It is said that on quiet summer evenings, you can hear a person singing...not just any person, but a woman with a high pleasing voice, a soprano...Jenny Lind, the world-famous Swedish entertainer. Lind stayed at the Gower House and is said to have stood on the balcony of the second floor and sung to a small crowd gathered below. Evidently, she was as enthralled as those who heard her, because she returns from time to time to Smithland, Kentucky, to grace the nearby waters of the Cumberland River with melody.

What an interesting way to end our journey on that fabled river!

Acknowledgements

The following books, articles and resources were used in the collecting and retelling of the ghost stories in this book:

Where Legends Live, A Guide to Cherokee Mythic Places; Douglas A Rossman: 1988; Cherokee Publications

Pegram Family Cemetery; the Haunted Places website; 2022

Hauntings of the Kentucky State Prison; Steve E. Asher; 2016, Permuted Press

Nashville Ghosts and Legends; Ken Traylor, Delas M. House, Jr.; 2007; The History Press

The Bell Witch of Tennessee; Charles Baily Bell, Harriet Parks Miller; 1930; Charles Eller, Bookseller

Ghosts Along the Cumberland- Deathlore in the Kentucky Foothills; William Lynwood Montell; 1975; University of Tennessee Press

The Gower House; Smithland, Kentucky

The Clement Railroad Hotel Museum; Dickson, Tennessee

Ft. Donelson National Military Park; Dover, Tennessee

Riverman; Jack Knox; 1971; Abington Press "Cumberland Legend"; John Lipscomb; June 8, 1947; the Nashville Tennessean

Hauntings and Legends of Cragfont; Ellen Wemyss, Louise Patterson; Sue Botsaris; 1992; Quality Printing

Trousdale, A Constitutional County; J.C. McMurtry; 1970; Vidette Printing Co

"The Lost Town of Cairo"; Ryan Baker; 2017

Old Sumner; Walter T. Durham; 1972; Parthenon Press

Steamboatin' on the Cumberland; Byrd Douglas; 1961; Kingsport Press

Trousdale County Historical Society Newsletter; July 2020

Slavery in the Clover bottoms; John McCline; 1998; University of Tennessee Press

True Irish Ghost Stories; John D. Seymour; 1914; Hodges, Figgis and Co.

A History of Scotland; John Duncan Mackie J.D. Mackie; 1984; Penguin Books

"The Campaign for Fort Donelson" National Park Service; 2020

Granville Ghost Walk; Historic Granville; 2022

"History, Memories, Ghosts Share Home"

Martha Highers; April 15, 1985; *The Nashville Tennessean*

Kentucky State Prison; Eddyville, Kentucky

About the Author

John Leslie Oliver is a retired teacher, artist and historian. As President of the Trousdale County Historical Society and a director of the county archives, he has read, collected, listened to, interviewed and visited much of Middle Tennessee and Central Kentucky.

While the story of pioneers is his specialty, it is his interest in ghost stories that has resulted in this book. In addition to three books on Trousdale County history, Oliver has written over one thousand articles on local history for his county newspaper.